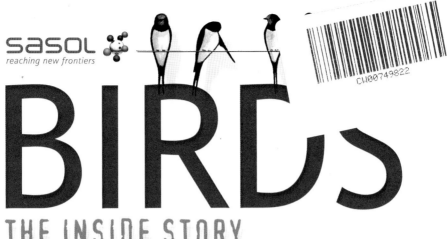

sasol
reaching new frontiers

BIRDS
THE INSIDE STORY

RAEL AND HÉLÈNE LOON

Struik Publishers
(A division of New Holland Publishing (South Africa)
(Pty) Ltd)
Cornelis Struik House
80 McKenzie Street
Cape Town
8001

New Holland Publishing is a member of
Johnnic Communications Ltd.

Visit us at **www.struik.co.za**

Log on to our photographic website
www.imagesofafrica.co.za for an
African experience.

www.imagesofafrica.co.za

IMAGES OF AFRICA
P H O T O   L I B R A R Y

First published in 2005

3 5 7 9 10 8 6 4

Publishing manager: Pippa Parker
Managing editor: Lynda Harvey
Editors: Helen de Villiers and Piera Abbott
Designer: Janice Evans
Cover design: Janice Evans
Illustrator: Hélène Loon
Proofreader: Glynne Newlands
Indexer: Mary Lennox

Reproduction by Hirt and Carter Cape (Pty) Ltd
Printed and bound by
Kyodo Printing Co (S'pore) Pte Ltd, Singapore

ISBN 978 1 77007 151 3

PICTURE CREDITS

Nigel Dennis: cover; title page; 9; 13; 19; 21; 25; 33b; 34b; 38c; 39a; 49; 60b; 72a; 78; 109b; 122; 124; 128; 132c; 134b; 143; 150a; 154b; 161; 169
Nigel Dennis/IOA: 27a; 28a; 30a; 31; 35a,b; 37; 38a; 42; 43a; 47; 52a,b; 54; 56a,b; 57b; 61; 67a,c; 72a; 117a; 133; 140b; 142b; 144; 150c; 159; 160; 172; 180; 182c; 189a,b; 190a,b; 192a; 194
Peter Steyn: 6; 20; 22a; 30b; 53a; 58c; 63; 69a,b; 75; 76a,b,c; 77; 88b; 93; 94a,b; 96a,b; 98a,b; 100; 101; 103b; 104; 105a; 106; 107a; 111a; 112a,b; 114b,c; 115b; 117b; 126; 132a,b; 134a; 135; 142a; 153; 163b; 166a; 173; 181; 182b
Warwick Tarboton: 28b; 36; 39b; 51a,b; 57a; 58a; 64; 65a; 66a,b,c; 67b; 68b; 72b; 73a; 79a,b; 82; 84; 87a,b; 88a; 89a,b; 92a,b; 95; 97; 103a; 108a; 120a; 125;151
Peter Pickford/IOA: 24; 29; 44; 70a; 80; 102; 105b; 115a; 140a; 145; 146; 163a; 166b; 195
R & H Loon: 27b; 33a; 41a; 50; 184; 185; 187a,b,c
Richard du Toit: sponsor's page; 8; 38b; 103c; 127; 157a
Roger de la Harpe/IOA: 71b; 154a; 182a; 192b
Shaen Adey/IOA: 14; 55; 190c; 35c
Nico Myburgh: 73b, 107b; 111b; 126
Keith Begg/IOA: 130b; 193
Colleen Begg: 155
Hugh Chittenden: 116; 118; 119

Martin Harvey/IOA : 22b; 32; 162
Mich Veldman: 65b; 99; 114a
Andrew Bannister/IOA: 136; 174; 191
Rita Meyer/IOA: 60a; 109a; 129
Peter Ryan: 15; 53b
Ian Michler/IOA: 70b
Hein von Horsten/IOA: 71a; 110
Tim Jackson: 130a; 131
Tony Camacho/IOA: 34a; 41c
Albert Froneman: 58b; 171
Chris Van Rooyen: 18; 62; 141
Malcolm Wilson: 41b
Frans Lanting: 168
Gerhard Dreyer/IOA: 43b
Colour Library/IOA: 68a
Peter Hancock: 108b
John Pilcher: 147
Mark Anderson: 33c
Carl Vernon: 120b
Steve Johnson: 150b
Colin Bell: 157b
Bob Bloomfield: 121
M & C Denis-Huot: 156
Courtesy of Van Riebeek Society,
Cape Town: 193a; 195b
Courtesy of Library of Parliament: 194a

CONTENTS

SPONSOR'S FOREWORD

Homo sapiens seems to thrive on acquiring secret facts – finding out the tantalizing story-behind-the-story.

The extensive collection of birding books sponsored by Sasol has stimulated a pastime locally that is among the fastest growing in the world. Yet, until now, there has been a need for a publication that really lifts the lid off birding, a book that goes beyond bird identification to enter the largely unexposed world of bird behaviour and biology.

This is exactly what *Sasol Birds – The Inside Story* does. In their book, Rael and Hélène Loon reveal a wealth of fascinating facts about the birdlife of southern Africa, from bird flight and the role of birds' feathers to bird senses, nest building, breeding, migration and even bird tracks.

We believe that this highly informative book will encourage active birders to become even more passionate about birding, and persuade prospective birders to join the flock. It is bound to become an indispensable companion book in our birding library. We are delighted to add *Sasol Birds – The Inside Story* to our list of environmental education publications.

Pat Davies
Sasol Limited Chief Executive

sasol
reaching new frontiers

ACKNOWLEDGEMENTS

We would like to thank the Struik team for the enormous effort, dedication and patience that went into this book. We are grateful to Pippa Parker for her continual guidance and support throughout the publishing process. We are indebted to Janice Evans for her painstakingly thorough attention to detail in layout and design, and her exceptional creativity that has brought the book to life. Helen de Villiers, Piera Abbott and Lynda Harvey are thanked for their great patience and expertise in editing the text. Thanks are also due to Colette Stott and Carmen Swanepoel for the daunting task of co-ordinating the photographic images sourced for the book.

Peter Ryan provided valuable comments and recommendations, for which we are grateful. We thank Malcolm Wilson, probably one of the most under-recognized ornithologists in South Africa, for his expert input. Margaret Sandwith from the Niven Library at the Percy FitzPatrick Institute of African Ornithology helped collate reference material. The sonograms were reproduced from *Roberts Birds of Southern Africa* with the kind permission of the trustees of The John Voelcker Bird Book Fund. Thank you to Sasol for providing sponsorship.

A number of professional photographers added flavour to the book. Thank you to Nigel Dennis and Peter Pickford for pointing us in the right direction. Peter Steyn and Warwick Tarboton are thanked for providing numerous photographs from their exceptional collections; Richard du Toit for, among others, his unique action shot of a chacma baboon catching an Egyptian Goose fledgling; Colin Bell for his unusual shot of a Woodland Kingfisher making a meal of a bat; and Peter Hancock for his remarkable image of a Lesser Jacana chick hiding underwater, using its bill as a snorkel. Thanks to Hugh Chittenden for his image of an Olive Sunbird feeding an Emerald Cuckoo chick pigeonwood berries; and Steve Johnson for his shot of orchid pollinaria attached to a sunbird's bill. Thanks too to Bob Bloomfield, Albert Froneman, Christine Denis-Huot, Frans Lanting Inc, Nico Myburgh, Mich Veldman, Keith Begg, Malcolm Wilson, Roger de la Harpe and John Pilcher for material used.

We wish to thank our families, particularly Rod, Adre, Hilton, Jacqui, Marc, Delia and Andrew, for their moral support and encouragement. Rod Marshall, in particular, has a tremendous reservoir of bird knowledge and has always been a big inspiration to Hélène to pursue her interest in ornithology. Thank you to Adre Marshall for assisting with the editing and Jacqui Loon for moral support and final finishing touches to some of the artwork. Thanks to both for babysitting while we compiled the book!

Finally, thank you to anyone else we may have overlooked, including the dozens of fellow birders who share our passion for exploring birdlife in southern Africa, and with whom we have exchanged bird anecdotes at one time or another.

PREFACE

Bird watching is much like stamp collecting – you don't really appreciate it until you already have some stamps in your collection to admire and compare. The more you acquire, especially if they are colourful or really unusual or rare, the more motivated you are to continue collecting.

Birds, though, unlike stamps, are three-dimensional and alive. They exploit the sky, and almost every other habitat on earth, they fly vast distances, sing, feed, court and breed, all in front of the fascinated eyes of the bird watcher.

Bird watching is one of the fastest growing hobbies in southern Africa. This ever-increasing interest in southern African birds, both by local and foreign enthusiasts, is reflected in the diversity of new material continually being devoted to the subject, from books, magazines and posters, to websites, tapes and high-tech CD-roms. Books are undoubtedly one of the most popular and necessary of these items, and cater for a diverse readership, from young children and laymen to enthusiastic and knowledge-able amateurs and professionals in the field of ornithology.

It may seem that there are almost as many bird books on the shelves as there are bird species in southern Africa, so one could justifiably question whether there is a real need, or indeed market, for yet another work! The answer is a resounding yes – within the vast plethora of bird books available, a distinctly vacant niche exists for an engaging, stimulating, more generalized bird book that goes beyond mere species

Hungry Cape White-eye chicks waiting to be fed

identification and highlights the many intriguing adaptations and fascinating aspects of bird biology and behaviour. The vast majority of bird books currently available are either field guides focused primarily on species identification, or impressive photographic coffee table books covering specialized interests. This book attempts to focus on the interesting and sometimes bizarre facts relating to birds in southern Africa.

For example, many avid birders may be able to identify a Rosy-faced Lovebird on sight or by its piercing call, but do they know that when building their nests, these remarkable birds carry their nesting material in the feathers on their backs, or that Palm-Swifts glue their nests together with sticky saliva? We look at nesting behaviour more closely, focusing among other things on the unique nest designs of the Cape Penduline Tit, the Hamerkop and Sociable Weavers' 'mansions'.

Many birders may have come across these or some other species' eggs while out in the field, but do they know why some birds lay speckled eggs, while the eggs of other species are pure white or even bright blue in colour? Or why some eggs are round, while others are distinctly pointed at one end? How did the peculiar habit of brood parasitism evolve in some birds and not in others?

Did you know that it is the African Jacana male rather than the female that plays the major role in parental care; or that the chicks take shelter under the adult's wings at any sign of danger? Did you know that the chicks of its relative, the Lesser Jacana, hide underwater using their protruding bills as snorkels to breathe until the coast is clear?

Did you know that different species of birds have very different wing and tail designs depending on their lifestyles? Do you know why albatrosses fly in distinct, zigzag flight patterns, how thermals are formed, or why some birds migrate and others choose to stay behind? Do you know why the legs of Marabou Storks appear to be whitewashed?

Do you know why nightjars have rictal bristles at the base of their mouths and special combs on their middle claws? Why birds sing at dawn? Or why they sing at all? Do you know why the tails of various widows are so long or how weavers woo their mates to their nests? Did you know that in some species, the male bird presents his partner with various 'nuptial gifts' in order to strengthen the pair bond?

This book attempts to answer these questions and many more.

The birding fraternity can generally be divided into two main groups – the 'twitchers', whose mission it is to tick as many bird species as possible off their checklist, and the so-called 'Zen birders', who are quite content to let the birds come to them. We hope this book will appeal to both camps and inspire readers to probe deeper into the fascinating life of the birds we so admire.

Rael & Hélène Loon
June 2005

1 MECHANISMS OF FLIGHT

Kelp Gulls in flight

WHAT AN INSPIRING IMAGE IS A BIRD IN FLIGHT! Its ability to take to the skies has captured the imagination of people throughout history, from scientists, writers and inventors to artists and mathematicians. The notion of flight has given rise to myths and legends across many cultures, and inspired the construction of many ingenious, though often ill-fated, flying machines. In the 16th century, Leonardo da Vinci predicted that '... man ... could subjugate the air and rise up into it on large wings of his own making'. After centuries of trial and often fatal error, man's dogged determination to overcome gravity eventually paid off, enabling us to take flight too.

However, despite the advanced technology of modern aircraft, bird flight still demonstrates an enviable, seemingly unattainable, effortlessness. Birds have exploited their ability to fly with considerable skill and success, reaching almost every continent and habitat on earth and flying thousands of kilometres on epic global migrations.

8

UNIQUE FLYING GEAR

Birds are the ultimate flying machines. Since their early reptilian ancestors first flap-glided rather clumsily on the planet over 150 million years ago, almost every aspect of bird biology has gradually been modified and honed to support their aerial ability. While we often take it for granted that a bird can fly, it is interesting to define exactly what it is that enables them to take to the air with such apparent ease. Birds have a number of special characteristics that set them apart from all other groups of animals, and which have made them such skilled aviators.

As light as a feather

Birds are unique in that they are the only animals on Earth that have feathers – a defining characteristic of the Class Aves. The combination of extreme lightness with exceptional strength and flexibility makes feathers highly efficient flying gear. These extraordinary structures have enabled birds to exploit the air and to come to represent the largest, fastest and most powerful flying animals on Earth. (*See also* Chapter 2, page 23.)

InSIDE InFO

FLIGHTLESS GIANTS

Ostriches are seven times too heavy to fly. Like other flightless birds they do not have a keel on their breastbones. Most birds have a pronounced keel to which their exceptionally large flight muscles are attached. This is why ostriches are known as 'ratite' birds, from the Latin word *ratis*, a raft, which their flat, keel-less breastbones resemble. Other ratites include the flightless rheas, emus and cassowaries. Ostriches, along with kiwis and tinamous, are the most ancient living birds.

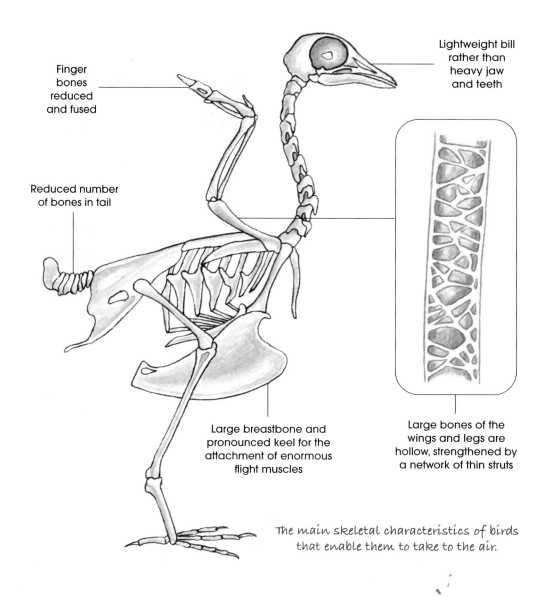

Finger bones reduced and fused

Lightweight bill rather than heavy jaw and teeth

Reduced number of bones in tail

Large breastbone and pronounced keel for the attachment of enormous flight muscles

Large bones of the wings and legs are hollow, strengthened by a network of thin struts

The main skeletal characteristics of birds that enable them to take to the air.

Light yet robust frame

For birds to take to the air, their bodies need to be as light as possible. To achieve this, their skeleton has gradually evolved a number of distinctive adaptations. Firstly, the long bones of the wings and legs (and, in larger birds, the spine) are hollow, strengthened by a delicate network of internal struts. They are therefore remarkably lightweight compared to mammal bones, which are filled with heavy marrow. Secondly, many redundant bones have been lost, while others have been fused together. As well as being lighter, this gives greater rigidity to the skeleton, which, in turn, cuts down on the weight of muscles, sinew and tendons that would otherwise be needed to hold the skeleton together.

Lightweight bills

During the bird's evolution, the heavy teeth and powerful jaws of their early reptilian ancestors were gradually replaced by the lighter bill structure of the modern bird. In addition to being light, a bird's bill still needs to be strong and, in many cases, flexible. It is made up of a finely strutted bone sheathed in a horny covering made of a tough protein called keratin. Depending on the species, the structure of the horny sheath may vary greatly: it may be equipped with cutting ridges, a hooked tip for tearing flesh, a horny plate for holding food or a number of other variations.

Advanced muscle power

Since flight is such a strenuous activity, birds have enormous, powerful wing muscles that can make up a third of their body weight. Two sets of muscles power the wings: the larger ones pull the wings down on the power stroke, while the other set lifts the wing on the upstroke. These large flight muscles are attached to a specially enlarged breastbone. Muscles used for persistent flight are darker in colour than those used for explosive bursts of flight.

Specialized air sacs

While bird flight might appear effortless to us, powered flight (as opposed to gliding and soaring) is, in fact, an incredibly strenuous activity that uses at least 10 to 15 times as much energy as sitting. Because of this, birds need vast quantities of oxygen to sustain flight. To aquire this extra oxygen, birds have evolved a unique breathing system – their lungs are linked to a specialized network of thin, bag-like air sacs throughout the body. Although these air sacs cannot actually extract oxygen from the air the way the lungs can, they help by storing air and controlling the flow of air through the lungs. This ingenious system ensures that there is a continuous, one-way flow of oxygen through the lungs, enabling the bird to receive oxygen both when breathing in *and* breathing out. A bird is therefore able to extract far more oxygen from each breath than a similar-sized mammal, which receives oxygen only when breathing in. The air sacs also help to cool the body, preventing overheating during high-energy flight.

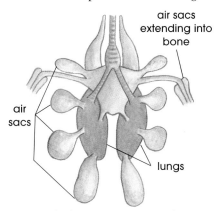

The specialized network of air sacs connected to the lungs enables birds to extract the large amounts of oxygen needed to sustain flight.

INSIDE INFO

SAVING BREATH

It is their unique breathing system, whereby specialized air sacs store and control the air through the lungs, that allows birds such as cormorants and grebes to remain underwater for long periods of time. This, together with special haemoglobin (*see* page 166), also plays a role in allowing migrating birds to fly at great heights where the oxygen is thin.

AERODYNAMICS

Leonardo da Vinci, who among his many celebrated achievements explored the scientific principles of flight, wrote in the 1500s that 'A bird is an instrument working according to a mathematical law'. Ever since Da Vinci's time, and perhaps even before that, scientists and inventors have been trying to understand and emulate the dynamics of bird flight. Although we are getting closer to unravelling the 'mathematical law' that Da Vinci speaks of, there are still many intriguing and unanswered questions that baffle even the experts.

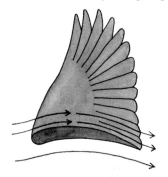

The aerofoil shape of the wing causes air to flow faster over the top, resulting in lift.

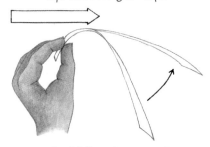

This lifting force can be demonstrated by blowing across the upper surface of a piece of paper, causing it to rise.

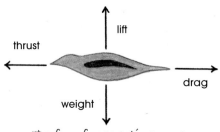

The four forces acting on a bird in flight are lift, weight, thrust and drag.

Some birds are more capable flyers than others. The effortless gliding of a lone Wandering Albatross above the ocean is very different from the awkward bursts of flight of francolins upon being flushed. Swallows and swifts are highly skilled flyers capable of intricate manoeuvres, in contrast to the Kori Bustard or Southern Ground-Hornbill with their heavy, ungainly flight. However, despite the diversity of modes of flight, all birds have the same set of equal but opposite physical forces to contend with if they are to stay airborne: lift and weight, thrust and drag.

Lift and weight

Birds can be described in aerodynamic terms. The cross-section of a bird's wing and main flight feathers is an aerofoil, like an aeroplane wing: concave below and convex above, with the leading edge blunt and rounded, and the trailing edge narrowing to a point. As air passes over the wing during flight, the convex shape causes it to flow faster over the top than under the wing. This causes lower pressure above the wing, which pushes the wing up and results in lift. So when a bird flaps its wings, it is not in order to push the air down and its body up as is often thought. Rather, it is the air passing over the wing surface as the bird moves forward that causes the bird to lift and overcome the opposite gravitational force of weight pulling it down.

Thrust and drag

While the aerofoil shape of the wing gives the bird the lift it needs to stay airborne, the beating wings propel it forward, maintaining the flow of air over the wing: this is known as thrust. In an aeroplane the engine fulfills this function.

During the down (or power) stroke, the primary feathers spread out like an opened fan, forming a solid surface that pushes against the air. On the upstroke, the wing closes slightly and the flight feathers separate as they twist in the air, allowing air to flow through the wing with little resistance. The wing is made up of two parts: while the inner wing is more rigid, the outer wing's 'wrist' and 'fingers' are more flexible and undergo changes in shape during the wing beat, providing most of the thrust.

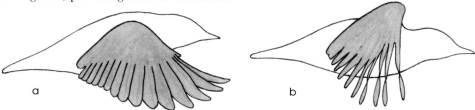

a   b

Feathers are fanned/spread during the down stroke (a),
but twist and separate during the upstroke (b).

In order to ensure 'flight safety', birds have evolved a number of fool-proof anti-stalling devices. This is necessary because, when a bird flies slowly to manoeuvre or land, a point is reached at which the friction of the air flowing over the wing surface creates turbulence. The drag caused by this turbulence may be greater than the lift on the wing, causing the bird to stall. While a bird's highly streamlined shape is one strategy to reduce drag, another is the evolution of a small but vital anti-stalling device on the wing called the 'alula'. The alula can be compared to flaps on plane wings, which are extended for slow flight.

An Egyptian Goose comes in to land with its alula raised to prevent stalling.

FLEXIBLE FEATHERS

One of the more subtle, yet vital keys to bird flight is the unique structure of the flight feathers, which allows them to change shape constantly through the wingbeat cycle. Each feather has a thin, firm leading edge and a broader, more flexible trailing edge. While the narrow leading edge remains firm, the flexible trailing edge changes shape automatically as the wing beats up and down, continually moving into the optimal position for flight.

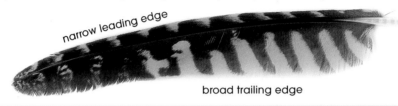

narrow leading edge

broad trailing edge

The alula, also known as the 'bastard wing', is a small but very important group of feathers growing from the wrist joint of the wing. The alula bleeds currents of air across the top of the wing, maintaining a smooth airflow and preventing the start of turbulence. By reducing turbulence and instability on the wing, especially during slow flight, the alula prevents a bird from stalling during take-off and landing. Without the alula, birds would lose the lift on their wings and would stall in mid-air as they slowed down to land, tumbling out of the sky in an undignified crash-landing!

A Verreauxs' Eagle comes in to land with full landing gear engaged: wings beating backwards, tail spread, alula raised and feet lowered.

Take-off and landing

How a bird takes to the air depends very much on how it is built and from where it is launching. When taking off from the ground, many birds simply jump into the air, giving their wings the room needed to beat and so taking flight. This is a much more difficult manoeuvre for large birds, however, and they usually have to taxi down a natural runway of water or open ground to gain enough speed to take off – a common sight when watching birds such as geese, cormorants, cranes and vultures taking to the air. Another less energetic launching method is for a bird simply to drop from a perch and spread its wings.

While taking off may use more energy, landing – especially onto a narrow perch – takes exceptional co-ordination and judgment. In order to touch down gently, a bird needs to slow down and lose height, but at the same time still keep enough lift to prevent it from stalling in mid-air. In addition to

A Shy Albatross 'runs' over the water surface as it is about to become airborne.

powering a bird, wings can also be used as brakes if they are flapped forwards, while lowering and spreading the tail is also an effective braking mechanism. As the bird 'touches down', it lowers its legs like the landing gear of an aeroplane. For extra protection, the legs of many species have a number of bones fused together to allow them to act as shock-absorbers on landing.

SKIMMING THE SURFACE

By flying close to the ground or water surface, many birds make use of what is known as the 'ground effect'. The air channelled between the bird's body and the water or ground surface reduces drag and enables the bird to expend less energy by either gliding or flapping less powerfully. This comes into effect when the bird's wings are less than a wingspan's distance above the surface, and it becomes more effective as the gap gets smaller. Shearwaters get their name from appearing to shear the water with their wingtips as they glide just above the surface. Many birds are thought to make use of the ground effect either when out foraging or flying long distances. For example, characteristic long lines of Cape Cormorants, often numbering thousands of birds, can be seen travelling low over the surface of the sea while ducks, skimmers and freshwater cormorants regularly fly just above the surface of inland waters.

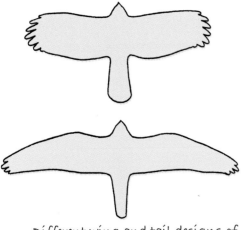

DIVERSE DESIGNS

Each bird species has evolved its own specific body, wing and tail shape, and these diverse designs allow different birds to exploit their own specific niches. By looking at these profiles, we can tell much about how a bird lives, including how it flies, finds and captures its prey and avoids predators.

Wing shape

Wing shape varies enormously from long and narrow to short and broad, with numerous shapes in between. The shape differs according to function and depends on the specific natural history of each species of bird.

Different wing and tail designs of goshawk (TOP) and falcon (ABOVE).

For example, while the African Goshawk and Peregrine Falcon are similar in size and both feed mainly on other birds, their contrasting flight shapes reflect their vastly different hunting methods.

The goshawk is shaped for manoeuvrability: its broad wings with the tips spread into 'fingers' and its long, broad tail enable it to pursue its prey between trees and dense foliage. In contrast, the falcon is built for speed with its long, pointed wings and narrow tail. Unlike the goshawk it hunts mainly in open areas, detecting its prey from a high vantage point such as a cliff face or from high in the sky and swooping down at a tremendous rate to make the kill, sometimes reaching speeds of over 300 km per hour.

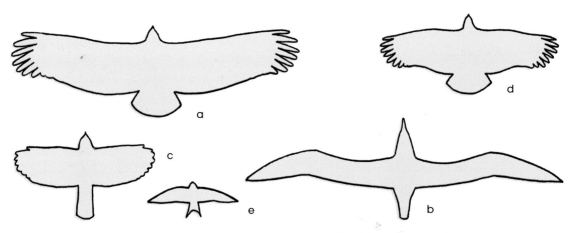

The shape of a bird's wing gives an indication of its flight style: (a) Large raptors have broad, 'fingered' wings ideal for soaring; (b) Many seabirds such as albatrosses, petrels and gannets have long, narrow wings for gliding; (c) The wings of most passerines are designed primarily for flapping flight; (d) Francolins and guineafowl have broad, stout wings for short, rapid bouts of fight; (e) Swallows and swifts have narrow, pointed wings for fast flight.

The forked tail of the Lesser Striped Swallow can be fanned and closed during flight, giving it greater control and manoeuvrability.

Tail design

When watching a bird flying, you will notice that its tail is continuously adjusted to help it steer, manoeuvre and brake, from subtle movements to drastic sweeps. The tail also helps to reduce turbulence and provide stability, particularly important in slow flight and during take-off and landing.

Tail shapes and lengths are as varied as the different species, from short and square to long and forked. Forked tails are characteristic of many aerial feeders, such as swallows, swifts rollers, drongos and bee-eaters, that need to be highly agile in chasing prey on the wing. By spreading and closing their tails like a fan as they fly, these birds are changing the surface area from large to small and back again, which gives them greater control and manoeuvrability.

INSIDE INFO

A SHORT TAIL

Although forked tails give great manoeuvrability, among the most agile of all birds are species with exceptionally short, square tails such as those of the spinetails and Bateleur. In these species, the extremely short tail makes the birds more unstable in flight, however. This instability allows for an increase in manoeuvrability in the air, making it easier for them to be deflected from their flight path at the last minute.

For example, Böhm's Spinetails move with extreme agility around their nests in baobab trees and when chasing their aerial prey. The Bateleur, which has a characteristically short tail (evidenced by the Afrikaans name *Stompstertarend*, or 'stump-tailed eagle'), is known for being extremely agile, with the distinctive habit of rocking from side to side in flight, hence its French name, *Bateleur*, which means 'acrobat' or 'tightrope walker'.

A SMALL FEAT

Swifts are unusual in that, being so well adapted to an aerial lifestyle, they have exceptionally small, weak feet and are, in fact, unable to perch. This is reflected in the generic name of many swifts, *Apus*, which comes from the Greek word meaning 'without feet'. When landing, they usually cling to the landing surface with all four toes facing forwards. Because they are unable to jump into the air swifts have little option but to take off by dropping from an elevated position. When migrating, swifts actually roost on the wing, and can remain airborne for more than six months.

FLYING STYLES

When watching birds in flight, you will notice that each species has evolved its own distinctive flying style. While some birds flap continuously, others intersperse bouts of flapping with gliding. Many small species seem to 'bounce' through the air in an undulating movement, while large raptors soar endlessly on broad wings without having to flap at all. Three broad types of bird flight are described here – **flapping, gliding and soaring**. Although most birds can be characterized by one main flying style, they may switch between different styles, depending on the situation.

Flapping

While flapping is the most common type of flight in birds, the rapid wing-beats mean that it is also the most draining, and birds use enormous amounts of energy to remain in the air. To get around this, two energy-saving techniques are used by many birds to 'freewheel' through the air.

The Great White Pelican alternates bouts of flapping with gliding to save energy.

A simple method of saving energy is for a bird to alternate flapping flight with bouts of gliding, as gliding is thought to use significantly less energy. The combination of flapping and gliding is also known as **undulating flight**, as birds lose height during the low-energy gliding phase, then regain height again while flapping, resulting in an undulating flight path. While many birds use this technique (bee-eaters, gulls, swifts, swallows, cranes and herons, among others), it is especially useful as an energy-saving device for larger birds flying long distances in search of food or on migration.

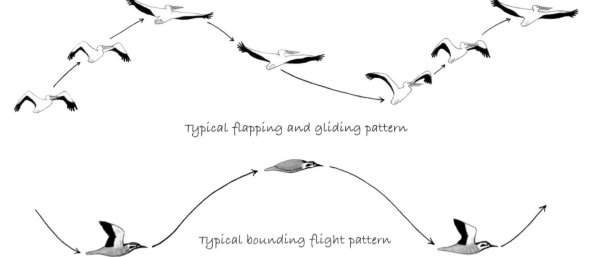

Typical flapping and gliding pattern

Typical bounding flight pattern

Small birds such as woodpeckers, wagtails, hornbills and thrushes are thought to save energy by what is called **bounding flight**. They close their wings completely and 'free-wheel' between bouts of flapping (rather than keeping them open as in flapping and gliding flight), giving them a 'bounding' flight pattern.

Gliding

Gliding flight is another low-energy means of transport, as it allows birds to travel long distances using **horizontal air currents** to propel them, rather than having to spend large amounts of energy flapping. Both the shape of the wing and the bird's size are good indications of a bird's ability to glide – the best gliders being fairly large birds with distinctly long, narrow wings. Most of the larger seabirds such as albatrosses, gannets, gulls and frigatebirds are ideally shaped for gliding for long periods of time.

HIGH-ENERGY HOVERING

By reversing the wingbeat on the upstroke, some birds use a specialized flapping technique, that of hovering. Because hovering uses more energy than normal flapping, most birds can't sustain it for long, hovering for only a few seconds while they look for or pick up food. Sunbirds hover briefly in front of flowers while they sip the nectar, and many insectivores hover momentarily while they pluck an insect from a leaf. Many small raptors and Pied Kingfishers hover for longer periods while they scan below for prey, usually making the most of headwinds to save energy and give them lift. Hummingbirds are masters of hovering and the only birds able to move backwards as well as forwards while hovering.

ALBATROSSES, THE ULTIMATE AERIAL SEAFARERS

The Wandering Albatross can fly thousands of kilometres without flapping its wings by using the ocean breeze to fuel its gliding flight.

Albatrosses are the ultimate aerial seafarers, even more at home on the open ocean and better adapted to its challenging conditions than the most seasoned sailor. They have evolved a specialized flying technique, known as 'dynamic soaring', that allows them to fly effortlessly for hours at a time without needing to flap their wings. They are able to accomplish this by making use of the wind gradient over the ocean's surface (wind speed is slower close to the surface due to friction). They follow a zigzag flight pattern, starting fairly high up and gliding at a rapid speed with the prevailing wind. They lose height gradually, gaining speed as they go, and when they finally near the water surface, they turn suddenly and bank upwards into the wind again, using the momentum from their fast downward glide to rise into the wind current. The Wandering Albatross lives up to its name, gliding with hardly a wingbeat over vast distances of up to 15 000 km at a time, and at speeds of up to 80 km an hour.

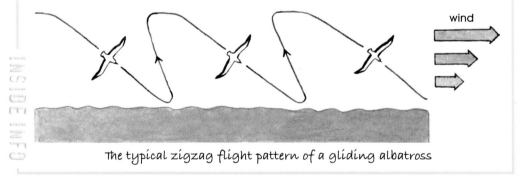

The typical zigzag flight pattern of a gliding albatross

As with an aeroplane, the bird generates lift as it moves through the air. However, in contrast to the fixed wings of a plane, birds are able to change the shape of their wings constantly, giving them greater control. This enables birds to glide at speeds that would be too slow to support them in the air if they had the inflexible wings of an aircraft. Many gliding birds are able to 'lock' their extended wings by means of a specialized tendon.

FEATHER 'FINGERS'

The primary feathers of the Bearded Vulture spread into 'fingers' during flight, an effect that is enhanced by the distinct emarginations at the feather tips.

The primary feathers of many birds have distinct emarginations, or indentations, near the tip. When the wing is spread, the primaries separate into what looks like individual 'fingers'. These 'fingered' wingtips are particularly prominent in large soaring birds with broad wings such as eagles, vultures, storks and pelicans. It has been suggested that each primary feather acts as a small, independent 'winglet' that twists in the air to maintain lift on the wing and so allow the birds to fly more slowly without stalling.

Soaring

In contrast to gliding, where birds use horizontal air currents to save energy, soaring relies on vertical air movements to save on high-energy flapping. True soaring is only possible for large, heavy birds such as raptors, storks and some seabirds. There are two main types of soaring:

Slope soaring occurs when seabirds such as gulls, albatrosses and cormorants take advantage of air currents deflected upwards against cliffs along the seashore. Slope lift is also produced inland when air is channelled upwards by a cliff or mountain and is used by large mountain dwellers such as the Verreauxs' Eagle and the Bearded Vulture.

Formation of a thermal: warm air rising from the heated ground forms swirling pockets of air, called thermals, that are used by large soaring birds to facilitate flight.

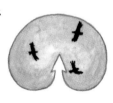

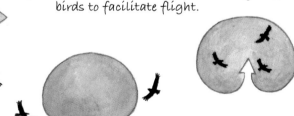

wind

By making use of thermals, large birds like African Openbills are able to soar for long distances without expending unnecessary energy.

A second source of energy for soaring is provided by **thermals**: pockets of air rising as they are warmed by the heating ground. Many large birds such as raptors and storks make use of thermals, spiralling in tight circles without a wingbeat to huge elevations of up to 2 000 m. By moving from one thermal to another, they can cover hundreds of kilometres a day with very little effort. These land soarers usually have broad wings and tails, enabling them to turn in tight circles, which is essential for staying inside thermals. Vultures use thermals to provide a vantage point from which they can scan the ground for carrion, while many large migrants use thermals to carry them on their epic journeys.

There are some disadvantages to relying on thermals, however. For example, many large birds are practically grounded on overcast days when there are no thermals to help them soar. Even on sunny days, birds have to wait for several hours after sunrise for the ground to heat up sufficiently, enabling thermals to form, before they can take to the air effectively.

FLYING IN A FLOCK

When watching large flocks of birds flying together, it is always a source of wonder how the entire flock co-ordinates the twists and turns in their flight path with such precision – and without colliding. It is thought that individual birds are so in tune with the movements of the other members of the flock that if one bird changes direction it results in a split-second ripple effect. Whole flocks are therefore able to synchronize their movements, banking and turning in the air with remarkable precision. Whatever the explanation, this phenomenon remains a wonder of the bird world.

An enormous flock of Red-billed Queleas moves in synchronized waves.

2 FEATHERS

FEATHERS ARE UNIQUE TO BIRDS. Engineered by evolution, their extreme lightness combined with exceptional strength and flexibility makes feathers the ideal flying gear. They constitute a truly multi-functional body-suit that is also adapted for numerous other functions. Feathers may act as hearing aids, water carriers, versatile all-weather gear or as dashing courtship finery. They can provide a camouflaged covering, rendering birds almost invisible, or their bright iridescent splashes of colour can turn heads.

FROM SCALES TO FEATHERS

Birds' feathers are thought to have evolved from reptile scales, and may have been used by birds' non-aerial reptilian ancestors for insulation. It is thought that some of these ancestors gradually took to the trees, and the scales slowly elongated, becoming rudimentary feathers that may have helped the early bird-like dinosaurs glide from branch to branch. Over time, the simple scale evolved into the complex feather that it is today.

Evidence of birds' reptilian ancestry can still be seen in the horny scales covering their legs and feet.

UNIQUE FORMS FOR UNIQUE FUNCTIONS

In the same way that we wear different garments on different parts of our bodies, so, too, do birds have a range of different kinds of feathers, each of which plays a special role.

Flight feathers are the long, firm feathers found on a bird's wings and tail. These feathers have a stiff, central quill from which the strong, flat surface of the feather (also known as the vane) grows. Flight feathers on the wing, also called 'remiges', are made up of both primary and secondary feathers. Flight feathers on the tail are called 'rectrices'.

Contour feathers cover the bird's body, overlapping like the scales of a fish and giving it a streamlined shape. They also help to protect and insulate the body.

Soft **down feathers** lie beneath the contour feathers of adult birds. They are designed to trap air, keeping the bird warm. Natal down is the first covering of feathers to develop in young chicks. Eider ducks from the northern hemisphere provide the exceptionally warm down used in duvets.

Filoplumes are thin, hair-like feathers found at the base of contour feathers. It is thought that they may act as minute sensory organs that pick up vibrations and movement, and cause the muscles controlling the contour feathers to respond.

FEATHERED FUNCTIONS

While the primary function of feathers is to allow birds to take to the air, the feathers of some bird species have evolved highly specialized functions that make them invaluable survival 'tools' to support the bird's idiosyncratic needs or habits.

▐ The flight feathers on the wings of many nocturnal owl species, such as the Barn Owl and Eagle-owls, are fitted with special **silencers**. The barbs on the leading edges of these feathers are unhooked, giving the feathers soft, comb-like fringes that break up the flow of air over the feathers during flight, muffling the sound of flapping wings. This allows the birds to remain silent as they swoop down to catch their prey.

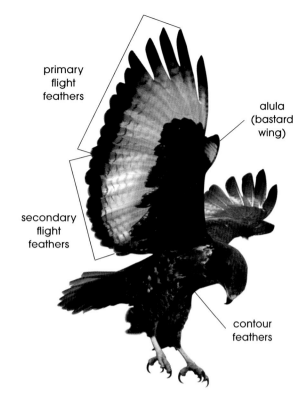

primary flight feathers

alula (bastard wing)

secondary flight feathers

contour feathers

Some of the different feather types can be seen on this Jackal Buzzard.

DESIGNED FOR FLIGHT

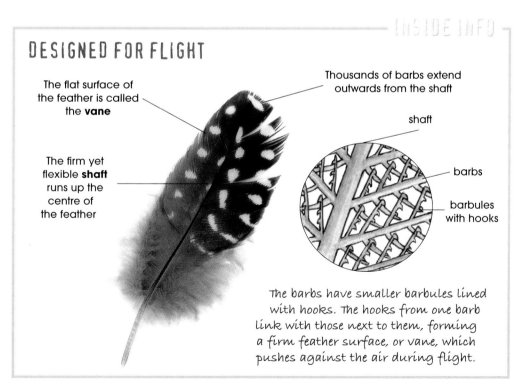

The flat surface of the feather is called the **vane**

Thousands of barbs extend outwards from the shaft

shaft

The firm yet flexible **shaft** runs up the centre of the feather

barbs

barbules with hooks

The barbs have smaller barbules lined with hooks. The hooks from one barb link with those next to them, forming a firm feather surface, or vane, which pushes against the air during flight.

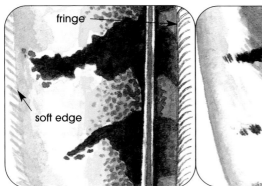

fringe

soft edge

The fringed edge of a
nocturnal owl feather

The unfringed edge
of an eagle feather

The comb-like fringe on the leading edge of the owl feather, together with the soft trailing edge, allow for silent flight. Eagle feathers, by comparison, lack the fringe, and have a firm trailing edge.

Small diurnal owls such as the Pearl-spotted Owlet, which feed mainly on invertebrates, do not have these fringes on their feathers as they don't need to make silent attacks; nor does the Pel's Fishing-Owl, as fish aren't highly sensitive to sounds above the water.

Sandgrouse live in arid habitats with very little available water. As they feed on dry seeds instead of insects, which have a high water content, the male birds have evolved specially adapted **water-holding belly feathers** which they use to carry water to their

FLIGHTLESS FEATHERS

Not surprisingly, the feathers of the Common Ostrich are not designed for flight: their barbules lack the hooks needed to bind them together into a firm surface. However, it was their soft, almost ethereal quality that first attracted the attention of early fashion designers, and turned the sleepy town of Oudtshoorn in South Africa into the hub of the feather industry. Although their feathers are no longer fashionable, ostriches continue to be farmed quite widely. Their feathers are still used as feather dusters, while their lean meat and high-quality leather are also sought after.

The feathers of the flightless ostrich lack barbules to keep the surface firm.

INSIDE INFO

A male Burchell's Sandgrouse soaks his sponge-like belly feathers before flying back to his thirsty chicks with his watery load.

thirsty chicks. These feathers have highly specialized barbules that allow them to hold three times as much water as normal feathers. After arriving at a waterhole, the male wades into the water and soaks his belly feathers, which absorb and hold water like a sponge. When the male returns to his brood, the chicks drink eagerly from his feathers. Males collect water in this way for about two months, until the chicks are able to fly to water themselves. Although the water is largely prevented from evaporating by a layer of feathers, some is nevertheless lost by the time the bird returns to his chicks. If he has to fly further than about 30 km, his entire precious watery load will be lost.

The tail feathers of the woodpecker are much stiffer and stronger than those of most birds, as they are specially **adapted to prop the bird up** and balance it while it is clinging to vertical tree trunks. The tail feathers have exceptionally stiff shafts, which are often further strengthened by firm ridges running along their length. Oxpeckers, too, have stiff tail feathers that support them as they cling to the hides of animals.

The strengthened shafts of a woodpecker's tail feathers help to prop it up against tree trunks.

Air trapped between the feathers of this Yellow-billed Duck help to give it buoyancy for floating.

Feathered 'eyes' at the back of the Pearl-spotted Owlet's head help to keep predators and mobs of small birds at bay.

The feathers of non-diving water-birds play an important role in giving them the **buoyancy needed to float**. Not only do these birds have light bodies, but their water-resistant feathers are able to trap air between them, particularly in the layer of soft down feathers. This layer of trapped air functions in a similar way to the air trapped in the hull of a ship, giving the additional lightness and buoyancy needed to float.

The Pearl-spotted Owlet is unusual in that it has 'eyes' at the back of its head – or so it seems at first glance or from a distance. These are actually just two dark rings of feathers. As in some moths, these **markings help deter potential predators** attacking from behind, as they are much less likely to attack if they think that they have been seen.

Many owl species, such as the Barn Owl and African Grass-Owl, have a characteristic facial disk, consisting of stiff feathers, that resembles a parabolic reflector. This **feathery disk helps channel sounds** towards the ears, improving the owls' ability to hear.

The facial disks of these African Grass-Owls channel sounds towards their ears.

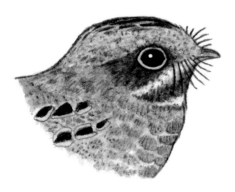

Stiff rictal bristles at the base of the nightjar's bill help to channel insects into its mouth.

The breeding season sees many birds undergoing a drastic 'change of image', when their drab non-breeding plumage transforms into **feathered finery**. For example, Southern Red and Yellow-crowned bishops' feathers become brightly coloured signals; Long-tailed and Red-collared widowbirds grow impressively long, flamboyant tail feathers; and the Pennant-winged Nightjar's inner primary feathers extend into extravagant streamers.

Many birds have specially modified feathers, in the form of **sensitive bristles**, that grow at the base of their bills. These bristles are particularly marked in the nightjars and swifts, and are thought to help the birds detect and channel insects into their beaks as they swoop in search of prey.

HOW MANY FEATHERS DOES A BIRD HAVE?

Record holders for the largest number of feathers are the swans, which have over 25 000. Small, perching birds such as robins, sparrows and weavers have between about 2 000 and 3 500 feathers. Hummingbirds have the fewest feathers, around 940.

FEATHER COLOUR

Birds exhibit a remarkable array of colours, their feathers showcasing the entire colour spectrum, often in shimmering, iridescent splendour. Surprisingly, the source of these diverse colours is often not what one might expect. For example, if a bird looks green, it does not necessarily mean that the feathers themselves are actually green in colour. And a puzzling question that many birders may have pondered is why the glossy, iridescent feathers of birds such as sunbirds and 'glossy' starlings turn a dull black when they move out of the sunlight.

white: absence of pigment and scattering

black: melanin pigment

green: scattering

red and orange: carotenoid pigments

blue: scattering

green: iridescence

blue: iridescence

grey: mixture of dark melanin pigment and white light from scattering

The origins of different feather colours are shown here in the White-fronted Bee-eater (LEFT) and the Southern Double-collared Sunbird (ABOVE).

What creates feather colour?

The colours of a bird's feathers are produced in two main ways.

The first is **pigment**. There are two main pigments that give feathers their colour: **melanin**, which produces either black or dark brown feathers; and **carotenoids**, which produce red, orange or yellow feathers.

Sometimes, a combination of different pigments results in a specific feather colour. The dull olive-green feathers of many woodland birds are produced by alternating yellow and brown pigments in the feathers.

Keratin also plays a role in feather coloration. It is the tough protein of which feathers are made, and is also found covering the bill, and in the scales and claws on birds' legs and feet. Translucent keratin reflects the light of a particular spectrum. Most feather colours not created by pigment, such as some blues and greens, are caused by the play of light in this keratin layer. When light hits the feather, the keratin reflects only

Sunlight is required to give feathers their shimmering, iridescent quality, as can be seen with this 'glossy' Greater Blue-eared Starling. The belly feathers in the shade have turned a dull black, as they need the sunlight to 'bring them alive'.

the relatively short wavelengths (or colours) of light, such as blues, greens and violets, and the rest are absorbed by the dark underlying melanin layer. So, although these feathers appear blue or green to us, it is not the actual feather colour that we see, but rather the coloured light reflected off the feathers' surface.

Keratin works in various ways, causing different effects depending on its structure. If the keratin is **layered**, the blue, green and violet colours reflected are known as **iridescence**. This can be found in the shimmering, often metallic feathers of the 'glossy' starlings and sunbirds, as well as in the flamboyant feathers of the peacock and the 'speculum' (coloured wing patch) of ducks. The generic name of the so-called 'glossy' starlings, whose plumage has a metallic sheen, is *Lamprotornis*, which comes from the Greek words *lamprotes*, meaning 'brilliance', and *ornis*, meaning 'bird'.

If the keratin is **dotted with air spaces**, on the other hand, the blues and greens are caused by a process known as **scattering**, and can be seen in the shimmering feathers of the Lilac-breasted Roller and the kingfishers.

In many feathers, colour results from a **combination** of pigments in the feather *and* light reflected by the keratin. For example, some non-iridescent green feathers are produced by a mixture of blue light produced by scattering and yellow carotenoid pigments in the feather, as found in many parrots. Grey feathers are caused by a combination of white light produced by scattering and by dark melanin pigment in the feather.

UNUSUAL PIGMENTS

Carotenoid pigments are derived from a bird's diet, and the characteristic pink of flamingo feathers comes from carotenoids found in the crustaceans and algae that the birds sieve from the water.

Apart from melanin and carotenoids, the only other feather pigments in the world are those found in the turacos. They have two pigments named specifically after them: a red pigment called 'turacin' and a green pigment called 'turacoverdin'.

BLACK POWER

In addition to colouring feathers, the dark pigment melanin gives them extra strength and durability. For this reason, the flight feathers of most birds are black, the strengthened feathers being more resistant to wear and helping them cope with the rigours of flight. This is especially true of migratory birds whose primary feathers have to endure the stresses of long and strenuous flights. White feathers, on the other hand, wear down much more easily.

ABOVE LEFT: The white tips of some of these Crested Barbet feathers have gradually worn away. ABOVE RIGHT: The flight feathers of most birds, such as these White Storks, are black, as the dark melanin pigment gives them strength.

Feather aberrations

In some rare instances, feather colour deviates from the norm, and confused birders are left wondering what they are looking at. Below are some examples of typical feather anomalies found in birds.

Leucistic Olive Thrush

▌ **Albinistic** birds lack pigment in their feathers because of a genetic inability to produce melanin. As a result, they are pure white. They also have red eyes, as well as pink legs and a pink bill. Albinism has been recorded in a number of bird species, including the Olive Thrush, Cape Bulbul, Malachite Kingfisher, Cape Sparrow and Fiscal Flycatcher, but these birds generally do not survive more than a few days, and are rarely seen.

▌ **Leucism** is the partial loss of pigment from a bird's feathers, making the plumage look lighter and more 'washed out' than normal, but not pure white. Leucistic birds do not have the red eyes and pink legs of albinos. Leucism has been recorded in many different birds species, from Blue Cranes to penguins, and does not generally affect their chances of survival. However, there are certain disadvantages to being leucistic.

Melanism is caused by an excess of black or brown pigment in the feathers, making the bird look dark all over. It is recorded regularly in the Gabar Goshawk, and in Ovambo and Black sparrowhawks.

Colour morphs also occur. In unusual cases, certain birds are born with feathers of a colour different from what is normal for the species. In southern Africa, the Crimson-breasted Shrike and the Black-collared Barbet sometimes occur in a rare yellow form – instead of bright crimson, the shrike has a yellow breast, while the characteristically red head of the barbet is yellow. Booted and Wahlberg's eagles have dark and light forms, while many owl species, such as the African Scops-Owl and Spotted Eagle-Owl, have both grey and rufous forms. These are much more common than the yellow forms mentioned above.

Tawny Eagle, showing two different colour morphs

Melanism, although rare, occurs more regularly in the Gabar Goshawk than in other birds.

The yellow colour morph of the Black-collared Barbet is rarely seen.

THE IMPORTANCE OF GOOD GROOMING

Because feathers are vital for a bird's survival, they need to be constantly groomed and kept in peak condition. Birds use a wide range of different methods to make sure that their feathers are always well maintained.

Preening

Preening is one of the most important ways in which a bird keeps its feathers in good condition. Birds have a preen gland at the base of the tail which secretes a fatty oil. Oil is spread by the beak over the feather surface, which helps to keep the feathers supple. This natural oil is also thought to reduce the growth of bacteria and fungi on the feathers and skin, while waxes in the oil act as a water repellant. Each feather is carefully drawn through the beak so that it is cleaned, and any separate filaments 'zipped' back together again. The long wing feathers are given extra care, as they are crucial for flight and undergo the most stress.

Not all birds have a preen gland. Ostriches have lost their preen gland over time, as their 'earthbound' feathers do not need to be groomed for flight. African Darters also lack a preen gland, and the absence of fatty oil allows their feathers to get wet – an adaptation to hunting underwater.

Birds such as the Saddle-billed Stork, Hamerkop and African Penguin keep their feathers in peak condition by preening regularly.

PREENING IDIOSYNCRASIES

So important is feather care that some birds have evolved a range of specialized grooming tools and techniques.

◢ Nightjars have evolved a **special grooming comb**, called the 'pecten', on the claw of the middle toe of each foot. The comb is used for preening the feathers, for scratching, and for removing parasites, as well as straightening out the long bristles around the bird's gape at the base of the bill, which are used to channel insects into the mouth. Herons, egrets, bitterns and cormorants have evolved a similar claw comb.

◢ Birds such as herons, egrets, bitterns, parrots and pigeons have evolved specialized feathers called **powder down**. The fraying ends of these feathers produce a fine, white powder that is spread over the feathers during preening and is thought to help groom and waterproof them. Powder down feathers are the only feathers that grow continuously throughout the bird's life, and are never moulted.

The fraying ends of the Cattle Egret's powder down feathers produce a fine powder that helps to keep the feathers in good condition.

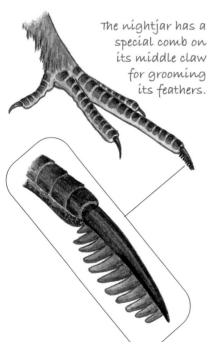

The nightjar has a special comb on its middle claw for grooming its feathers.

◢ In Green Wood-Hoopoes, the preen gland has an additional function. It produces a foul-smelling scent that is used as a defence mechanism to deter potential predators – a unique form of **chemical warfare**. The odour warns predators that the birds not only smell bad, but are also unpalatable. Buttonquails and the African Hoopoe are also notorious for being rather malodorous.

◢ In some bird species, one individual will preen another bird's feathers, an activity known as **allopreening**. The focus is usually the feathers around the head, which a bird cannot reach itself. In addition to helping keep these feathers in good condition, allopreening is thought to have an important social function, and usually occurs between mates or close relatives. The preener is usually the more dominant bird, and allopreening may be a way of asserting this dominance. In the breeding season, a male will often allopreen a female as part of the courtship process.

Bathing

For birds, bathing is an important way of keeping their feathers clean and in good condition. Birds not only soak their feathers in water, but also have dust baths, bathe in the warmth of the sun's rays and, rather oddly, allow waves of ants to swarm all over their feathers.

WATER-BATHING

In addition to helping keep feathers clean and make them more flexible and pliable for preening, many birds living in hot, arid areas bathe as a means of cooling down. Among fish-eating birds, bathing is important as it helps to wash off the slimy mucus from their fish prey that can dirty and damage their feathers. Birds' feathers may become quite soaked while bathing, making it difficult for them to fly immediately afterwards. The bird then 'flap-flies' heavily to a safe place, shakes its feathers vigorously, then preens, scratches and dries off.

Many aerial feeders such as bee-eaters, swallows, swifts, drongos and nightjars, do not land and bathe. Rather, they plunge briefly into the water during flight, while kingfishers **plunge-bathe** from their perch above the water. This is by far the safer option since these birds have short, weak legs, making them slower to launch off the ground than most birds. This delay in taking off, compounded by wet feathers, would make them more vulnerable to predators if they were to land to bathe.

Some birds, such as white-eyes, warblers and hornbills, **leaf-bathe** in water that has collected on rain- or dew-soaked foliage. Depending on the size of the bird, they either dip into the water caught in big leaves, or shake themselves against bunches of smaller leaves, wetting their feathers.

White-faced Ducks engaged in allopreening.

Birds such as this Little Sparrowhawk often bathe to clean their feathers or to cool down in hot weather.

Some birds make the most of the rain, standing with their feathers ruffled and wings and tail spread out to catch the falling drops. Birds can often be seen **rain-bathing** under sprinklers in the garden.

SUNBATHING

Many birds take advantage of the warm rays of the sun, with different species taking up different sunbathing postures. Smaller birds lie on the ground with their wings and tail spread, and often raise the feathers on their back. Larger birds such as cormorants, African Darters, storks and herons stand with their wings held open. However, while cormorants and African Darters sun the uppersides of their wings, herons stand with the undersides facing into the sun. Birds usually preen vigorously after sunbathing.

The warmth of the sun's rays is thought to soften old preening oil on the feathers and cause skin and feather parasites to move around, making them easier to remove. Ultra-violet rays kill potentially harmful bacteria on the feathers. Sunlight may also help synthesize vitamin D, as well as helping flight feathers to maintain their optimal shape.

For a number of bird species, sunbathing takes on a more specialized role in feather care. A bird's flight feathers, particularly those of large birds such as raptors and storks, can become slightly bent or bowed out of shape with the constant **stresses of flying**. The warmth of the sun's rays acting on the feathers can help to restore their shape.

Marabou Storks sun themselves with their wings held open for maximum benefit.

The African Darter can often be seen with wings spread, sunning its drenched feathers.

Flight feathers bent out of shape by the rigours of flying are restored through sunbathing.

While most waterbirds trap a layer of air between their contour feathers to help them float, cormorants and African Darters, on the other hand, intentionally raise the feathers on their bodies when swimming, which allows water to flow between their feathers and soak them. Ironically, getting their feathers wet is actually an advantage for these birds. The low buoyancy means that they don't need to use up as much energy to stay underwater when diving. They can remain submerged for longer periods of time, and can dive further in search of food that other waterbirds would be unable to reach. When they emerge, their drenched plumage needs to be **hung out to dry**, a process that also warms the bird after its swim in cold water.

Mousebirds often look as though they are covered in ruffled fur rather than sleek feathers. This is because the outer parts of the feathers on their head and body do not have barbules to keep the vane together, and so look scraggly and unkempt. Because

Speckled Mousebirds look ruffled as their outer body feathers lack barbules.

of this, mousebirds are more prone to getting wet, and are often seen **sunbathing after bad weather**. They avoid water-bathing, as over-wet feathers would impair their flight. Mousebirds also sunbathe after meals to speed up the bacterial fermentation of their primarily vegetarian diet. Mousebirds usually huddle closely together in groups when roosting at night in order to retain warmth.

DUST-BATHING

Many species, especially ground birds such as francolins, guineafowl and sandgrouse, as well as smaller birds such as sparrows and mousebirds, have regular dust baths. This process is similar to water-bathing in that it entails crouching down in a sandy area and flinging fine soil over the feathers. Dust-bathing is thought to help dislodge harmful parasites from the feathers, and to get rid of excess preen oil.

Anting

Anting is a highly unusual and intriguing activity where birds crouch on the ground and encourage hundreds of ants to swarm busily across and between their feathers. They may also pick ants up in their beaks and rub them across their feathers. Although this behaviour is still somewhat of a mystery, it is thought that the formic acid produced by ants may act as an effective parasite repellant, as well as possibly helping to remove old preen oil from the feathers.

FEATHER REFURBISHMENT

Even with the best care, feathers do eventually become old and worn through natural wear and tear. They have to be replaced at regular intervals by a complete set of new, strong feathers in a process known as **moulting**. This energy-intensive process usually occurs after the breeding season.

In addition to replacing worn or damaged feathers, moulting also marks the 'coming of age' ritual for young birds changing from their juvenile feathers into their mature adult plumage. For many bird species, moulting can also bring a change of image, as it allows male birds to transform into their bright display plumage for the breeding season, and then back again into their dull, non-breeding plumage afterwards.

When a bird moults, new feathers (TOP) replace old worn feathers (ABOVE).
RIGHT: A Helmeted Guineafowl feather just emerging from the 'pin'.

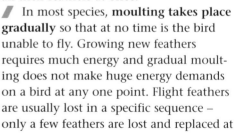

How long does it take a bird to moult?

The time a bird takes to moult varies greatly from species to species; while most birds moult their flight feathers gradually and in a fixed sequence, others have a more dramatic approach and lose all their feathers at once.

In most species, **moulting takes place gradually** so that at no time is the bird unable to fly. Growing new feathers requires much energy and gradual moulting does not make huge energy demands on a bird at any one point. Flight feathers are usually lost in a specific sequence – only a few feathers are lost and replaced at

A new feather is emerging from the pin of this Emerald-spotted Wood-Dove.

The tail of this juvenile Lesser Kestrel is moulting into its adult plumage.

a time. They are also usually lost in pairs – one from the right side and one from the left; but this is not always the case. While some species take about three months to moult, others take as long as six to nine months. Some of the larger raptors are in a state of slow, continuous moult; by the time one moult ends it is time for the first feathers moulted to be replaced again.

On the other hand, some species such as ducks and geese may **lose all their flight feathers at one time**, rendering them completely flightless during the three- to four-week period that it takes them to achieve their complete 'makeover'. During this vulnerable period they either move to areas that are safe from predators, or take refuge on the water if threatened. Luckily, these birds are not dependent on flying to find food, but forage on the land and in the water in a limited area. Also, in preparation for their moult, they put on weight and eat foods that contain the nutrients necessary for the growth of new feathers.

African Penguins also moult all their feathers at one time, a process that takes about 20 days. Because waterproofing is lost during moult, penguins are unable to go to sea during this period. They spend weeks fattening up before coming ashore, putting on as much as 30 per cent of their initial body weight, and survive off these stored fat reserves while land-bound.

During the breeding period the males of certain hornbill species wall the females into their nests. They use this period of flightless incarceration to moult their entire set of wing and tail feathers, so that they are freshly feathered when they eventually do emerge.

How often do birds moult?

The frequency with which birds need feather refurbishment depends on the species. While most species moult their entire plumage only once a year, others need to moult more often. Second and third moults are usually of body feathers only, and not of flight feathers. Birds that display during the breeding season moult their body feathers twice a year. Birds that spend much time in the water, such as ducks and geese, usually have to moult twice a year as well to keep feathers in good condition.

African Penguins lose their feathers all at once, remaining land-bound during this period.

3 BIRD SENSES

African Spoonbill

BIRDS EXPERIENCE THE WORLD AROUND THEM FROM A VERY DIFFERENT PERSPECTIVE TO OURS. Most birds have exceptional panoramic vision, allowing them to see almost 360° around. They are also able to detect subtleties of sound that our ears would not discern; and they use their sensitive beaks rather than hands to catch, dig and probe. Although we may inhabit the same world as birds, we experience it very differently.

Although birds have the same range of senses as other vertebrates, theirs have been honed to cope with the demands of their aerial lifestyle, allowing them to fly and effectively judge distances, to find food, detect and avoid danger, and recognize and secure a mate.

It's useful for us to try to appreciate a bird's quite different view of the world if we wish to understand and interpret its behaviour. In this chapter, we will look through the sharp, penetrating eyes of an eagle; hear through the acutely sensitive ears of a nocturnal owl; investigate the sensitive tip of a Yellow-billed Stork's bill as it probes into thick mud in search of its prey; and learn how some pelagic birds use their sense of smell to find food.

Vision: a bird's-eye view

While birds rely on all five of their senses, vision and hearing – both crucial for a bird's survival – are the most highly developed.

Excellent vision is a vital prerequisite for flight: birds need to make continual, rapid reassessments and accurate adjustments as they travel at speed through their environment.

What makes a bird's eyes unique?

Although the basic structure of birds' eyes is similar in many ways to that of other vertebrates, they have a number of unique and distinctive features that make for highly developed eyesight.

Birds have **enormous eyes** relative to their body and brain size. Each eye is often as big as, or bigger than, the brain, an indication of how important vision is to their survival. Birds' eyes do not appear obviously big because most of the eye is hidden behind the eyelids. The real size of the eyes can be seen by examining a bird's skull, which shows the huge eye cavities.

The Goliath Heron has acute eyesight needed to capture its elusive prey.

pigeon   squirrel

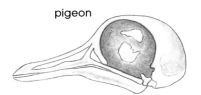 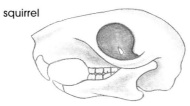

The eye cavity of a bird's skull is much larger than that of a similar sized mammal.

The eyes of some raptor species are as big as adult human eyes – enormous, when you compare the difference in body size – while the eyeball of the Common Ostrich has a diameter of about 5 cm, which is comparable in size to that of large land mammals. The advantage of large eyes is that a bigger image is able to form on the retina, which allows more detail to be seen.

The Common Ostrich has the biggest eye of all birds.

The true eye size of the Cape Robin-Chat can only be seen when looking at the enormous eye cavity of the skull.

Raptors, such as this African Hawk-Eagle, have exceptionally acute eyesight.

The retina of a bird's eye is also unusual in that it contains **special coloured oil droplets**, which may be shades of red, orange, yellow or green. The oil droplets act like little light filters, filtering out certain colours and making birds' eyes more sensitive to colours that would be useful to them in finding food. For example, in birds such as seed-eaters, the filters make their eyes more sensitive to colours in the red/orange/yellow range which would be useful in detecting seeds, while in birds that fish underwater, the droplets allow them to see better in blue and green light.

Birds' eyes have the advantage of being packed with significantly **more visual cells** than those of most other animals. The retina, which is the 'screen' at the back of the eye onto which the image falls, contains two different kinds of visual cells: rods and cones. The rods are sensitive to *light*, while the cones are sensitive to *colour*. These visual cells are most highly concentrated in an area called the **fovea**, a small depression in the centre of the retina where vision is clearest. Raptors are particularly well equipped with these visual cells, having as many as one million visual cells in the fovea, compared to only about 200 000 in our eyes. This gives them superior vision and allows them to see in much greater detail.

Birds' eyes contain a special structure called the **pecten**, which is found on the inner side of the eyeball that leads onto the optic nerve. The pecten improves the bird's vision as it has a special network of blood vessels that provide an important source of extra nutrients to the retina, which does not contain blood vessels itself.

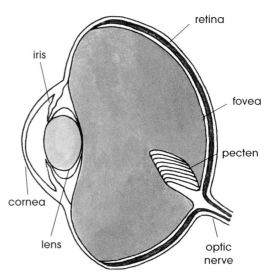

The internal structure of a bird's eye

Because birds fly at such speed, they have evolved the ability to **process information very rapidly** from the environment around them. In addition to being important for everyday activities, this exceptional ability allows swallows and swifts to catch insects in the air as they speed past on the wing, while many birds are able to manoeuvre through dense foliage without colliding with branches or leaves.

Colour vision

Although birds see the world around them in colour, they are thought to be able to see a wider range of colours and hues than we do, and many can see in the ultra-violet spectrum that is not visible to our eyes. One reason for this **enhanced ability to see colour** is that birds have more colour-sensitive pigments in their eyes than we do. While we have three different pigments in our cone cells (people who are colour blind have just two), birds have between four and five, allowing them to see a broader colour spectrum.

Although it is known that all diurnal birds have good colour vision, it was once thought that nocturnal species such as owls and nightjars could see only in black and white. However, this is now known not to be the case. Although nocturnal birds do not have the excellent colour vision of most diurnal birds, as many of their colour-sensitive cone cells have been replaced with light-sensitive rods, their vision is not totally monochromatic.

FOOD AND COLOUR

Colour vision is vital to birds in their search for food. Birds that feed on fruit (frugivores) are able to tell by its colour whether the fruit is ripe or not, while nectar-feeding birds (nectarivores) are attracted to flowers by their colours – generally speaking, most flowers that are pollinated by birds are red and orange. Colour is also important to insect-eating birds (insectivores) as they use colour to distinguish between edible insects and those with garish coloration, which warns that they are toxic.

Birds' colour vision allows them to identify the garish colours of these insects as a sign of their toxicity.

Blister Beetle

Caterpillar of Monarch Butterfly

Monarch Butterfly

Seeing in the ultraviolet

Many bird species are able to see the world through an additional colour dimension: they have a special pigment in their cone cells that allows them to see ultraviolet light. Although little research has been conducted specifically on the ability of southern African birds to detect UV light (most studies have focused on North American and European birds), it is likely that many southern African species do have this ability.

Some mystery still exists as to what exactly ultraviolet vision is used for, but the following are thought to be some of its possible functions:

/ Many fruits that rely on birds for dispersal attract their attention by developing a waxy bloom that reflects UV light when ripe.

/ The patterns on many flowers and leaves are more distinct in UV light. It is thought that they guide birds that feed on fruits or nectar to the plant, which in turn encourages pollination and seed dispersal.

/ In the northern hemisphere, kestrels can detect the urine trails of voles, as urine absorbs UV light. This helps them in tracing and catching their prey.

/ It has been found that the plumage of certain bird species reflects UV light. In these species, the feathers of male and female birds appear different in UV light, and it is possible that this may be used by birds in assessing and choosing a mate.

/ It is possible that birds might use UV vision when navigating on migration. UV light can pass through clouds, and so may help migrating birds to identify the position of the sun, enabling them to navigate even on cloudy days.

Nocturnal vision: eyes that 'see in the dark'

Contrary to what is often believed, nocturnal birds such as owls and nightjars cannot see, any more than we can, when it is completely dark. However, they are able to see under exceptionally low light conditions where most mammals would not be able to see anything at all, enabling them to hunt effectively under moonlight or if there are stars in the sky.

In order to allow more light to enter the eye, nocturnal birds tend to have much larger eyes than diurnal birds and are also able to dilate their pupils until they are very wide. In addition, their eyes contain a much higher concentration of light-sensitive rods than those of diurnal birds. However, the image that nocturnal birds see is thought to be grainy compared to the sharp image seen by diurnal birds. This is because their visual cells are situated further apart in the eye, which allows them to gather as much light as possible in dark conditions.

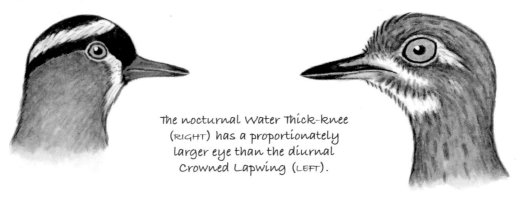

The nocturnal Water Thick-knee (RIGHT) has a proportionately larger eye than the diurnal Crowned Lapwing (LEFT).

Their eyes are also highly sensitive to movement as opposed to shape, so a mouse crouching quietly on the ground below an owl might go undetected until it gives itself away by making the fatal mistake of moving. Owls also rely on exceptional hearing in order to help them locate their prey.

Different perspectives (monocular vs binocular vision)

Interestingly, not all birds see the world around them from exactly the same perspective. Different species have entirely different 'world views', depending largely on whether their eyes are positioned at the sides or in front of the head. This, in turn, depends on the way in which particular birds find their food, and their need to look out for predators.

'Monocular' vision describes the area seen by one eye only, while 'binocular' vision is the area where the two monocular fields of each eye overlap to form a single image. Although all birds have both monocular and binocular vision, the size of each field varies greatly between different species.

Nearly all birds, apart from raptors, have **large monocular fields** and small binocular fields of vision. With eyes situated at the sides of their heads, they can see

almost all the way round without having to look up or move their heads from side to side. These birds are all potential prey species, and so, in order to detect predators arriving from any direction, it is vital for them to have maximum panoramic vision at all times. This wide-angle view is also useful for detecting prey and, among gregarious birds, for keeping an eye on the movements of the group.

The front and side views of a Kurrichane Thrush and Spotted Eagle-Owl clearly show that the thrush's eyes are positioned at the sides of its head, while those of the owl face forward.

The Spotted Eagle-Owl's huge eyes are particularly sensitive under low light conditions.

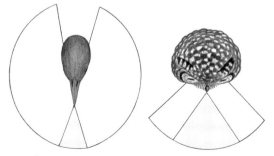

While the thrush has a small binocular and large monocular field, the owl has a significantly larger binocular field and a smaller monocular field.

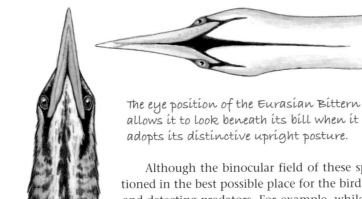

The Cape Gannet's eyes are located at the sides of its head, enabling it to look down at the sea as well as straight ahead without having to move its head.

The eye position of the Eurasian Bittern allows it to look beneath its bill when it adopts its distinctive upright posture.

Although the binocular field of these species is very small, it is positioned in the best possible place for the bird in terms of both finding food and detecting predators. For example, while herons and egrets have wide fields of monocular vision, their binocular field is in a narrow strip where they need it most: in front of the beak and down to their feet, where they are most likely to catch their prey.

The eyes of raptors, like ours, are positioned at the front of their heads. Because of this, the fields of vision of each eye overlap more than in other birds, creating **larger fields of binocular vision**. Binocular vision allows a bird to judge distances more accurately and to see more clearly and in better detail than monocular vision. The binocular field is usually in front of and around the beak, as well as in a band above and below it, which assists in catching prey. Their sideways fields of monocular vision, however, are more limited than those of other birds.

The third eyelid: A bird's natural windscreen-wiper

All birds have a third eyelid, the nictitating membrane, which sweeps sideways across the eyeball like a windscreen-wiper, helping keep the eye moist and clean. In some species the membrane is transparent and the bird can see through it clearly, while in other species it

---

INSIDE INFO

EAGLE EYES

A large binocular field is particularly important to raptors for a number of reasons:

- It enhances their ability to estimate depth, and to judge ever-changing distances when swooping to catch their living prey.
- It is thought to help them with precision flying: a large binocular area up front might help them to make sudden changes in direction and speed.
  - Raptors hold and manipulate their food with their talons. Binocular vision allows them to look at and focus on the prey that they are holding without having to turn their heads sideways.
  - Raptors have tubular eyes, with the large lens lying closer to the retina, allowing for more acute vision. A disadvantage of the tubular shape is that it renders the eyes almost immobile and unable to swivel. The birds compensate by having highly flexible necks that allow them to look around.

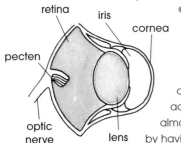

retina · iris · cornea · pecten · optic nerve · lens

REMAINING FOCUSED

You may have noticed that birds often bob their heads back and forth when walking. Although this appears to be a rather dizzying activity, there are certain advantages to it. The head bobs forward rapidly, then stays still while the legs move the body forward to catch up with and over-take the head. The head then bobs forward again, and so the bird continues on its way. The head stays in one place for as long as possible, which allows the bird to see more clearly. If its head moved continuously, its vision would constantly be blurred. Ballerinas use a similar princi-ple to avoid becoming dizzy while doing pirouettes, turning their heads rapidly only at the end of each rotation.

For the same reason, birds sitting on a branch moving in the wind try to keep their heads as still as possible while their bodies move with the swaying of the branch. This is also true of birds such as the Black-shouldered Kite when hovering in windy conditions – they keep their heads as still as possible while their bodies are buffeted by the wind.

is opaque. Nictitating membranes are also found in most amphibians and reptiles.

In certain birds this special third eyelid also serves as diving goggles or a windscreen:

/ In underwater hunters such as darters and cormorants the third eyelid functions as a pair of **diving goggles**. Being able to close this transparent third eyelid for pro-tection allows these birds to keep their eyes open underwater so that they can see and pursue their prey.

/ The third eyelid is also thought to act as a **'windscreen'** to protect birds' eyes when they fly at high altitudes where the air is cold, and it is especially valuable to migratory species flying long distances. It

The African Darter's third eyelid functions as a pair of diving goggles when it hunts underwater.

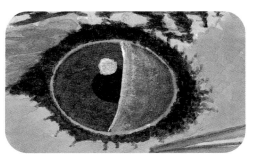

The third eyelid, or nictitating mem-brane, serves to clean and protect a bird's eye.

also acts as an important eye-protection layer for many birds when they are feed-ing. For example, in seed-eaters, it closes on reflex as the birds thrust their heads downward to peck at the ground, protect-ing the eye from any dust or particles that could fly up.

EYE COLOUR

Eye colour varies greatly from species to species: some birds have brown eyes, while the eyes of others may be red, orange, yellow, blue, white or black. Eye colour itself, however, does not seem to play an important role in influencing the quality of a bird's vision, although different coloured eyes may be more sensitive under different light conditions. Interestingly, eye colour can be an indication of a bird's sex and age. In some bird species the male and female have different eye colours. For example, the male Saddle-billed Stork has brown eyes while the female's eyes are bright yellow, and the male Southern Masked-Weaver has bright red eyes compared to the brown eyes of the female.

In many species, eye colour changes as the bird matures, with juveniles having a different eye colour to that of adults. Bird ringers use this as a means of aging birds that they catch and ring. In certain species, eye colour changes between the breeding and non-breeding season.

Hearing: sound sense

Sound is vital for communication between birds: the harsh, grating alarm call warning of danger, the flamboyant song of a male to attract a mate, the persistent call of a chick begging to be fed. Sound can also alert a bird to the whereabouts of potential prey. Because sound is so important for survival, birds need to be able to discriminate between the different kinds of sounds that they hear in order to interpret their meaning. To do this, they have evolved exceptionally acute hearing.

Acute hearing

Although birds and people hear sounds over a roughly similar range, the hearing of birds is more accurate than ours in many ways. Birds are able to distinguish between slight variations in sounds that our ears would not be able to detect. For example, where we might listen to a bird's call and hear only a single note, a bird would hear up to 10 separate notes. This extraordinary ability enables them to identify other individual birds by their specific calls, and in many species, females choose a mate based on the quality of his song.

Unlike humans and most other mammals, birds don't have an external ear, or 'pinna'. Rather, the ear opening is a simple hole behind the eye, and is covered by a layer of feathers. It is thought that external ears never evolved in birds as they would cause extra friction during flight.

The earhole of a Rattling Cisticola

The hearing of this Barn Owl is 300 times better than that of a pigeon.

Owls: masters of hearing

Owls are well known for having excellent hearing. They have been shown to have more acute hearing than diurnal birds, and their hearing is said to be about 300 times better than that of the average pigeon. However, contrary to popular wisdom, their special ability is not to hear very soft sounds (most other animals, including people, hear almost as well as most owls do). Rather, their reputation for excellent hearing stems from their exceptional ability to pinpoint very accurately the location of noises in the dark. They are especially sensitive to sounds with a high frequency, such as the rustling of dry leaves, that would give away the presence of potential prey.

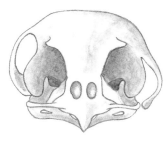

The ears of many owl species are asymmetrically placed in the skull. This is thought to improve hearing.

■ A number of owl species, such as African Grass and Barn owls, have their own **natural parabolic reflectors** in the form of round facial discs. These discs reflect and channel sound towards the ear, enhancing the bird's hearing.

■ In some owl species, the **ears are positioned asymmetrically** in the skull, with the left ear higher than the right. This unusual ear arrangement is thought to help the owl localize sound, and accurately detect the position of its prey in the dark.

■ Some owl species, such as the Barn Owl, have **movable flaps of skin next to their ears** that they can move and adjust to improve the detection of sounds coming from any direction.

Touch and taste

A wader probing, staccato-like, in a mudflat; a duck dabbling frenetically at the bank of a pond; a skimmer slicing the glassy surface of a river; and an avocet systematically scything its beak this way and that through the shallows – all these birds are employing their own means of searching for food under water or under mud. How do these birds 'see' what they are looking for, and how do they know whether the morsels that they find are edible or not?

In muddy water the Yellow-billed Stork uses its highly sensitive bill, rather than sight, to locate its prey.

Feeding by feel

Although it would seem that taste and touch are not well developed in the majority of birds, the degree of sensitivity in the bill and tongue depends largely on how a bird feeds. Researchers have found that birds that rely heavily on their beaks for foraging have bill tips and tongues that are densely packed with sensitive touch receptors called 'Herbst corpuscles', which are **sensitive to both taste and touch**. This sensitivity in the bill allows these birds to locate potential food purely by touch, and to assess whether it is edible, without having to see it. So if a wader finds an object while probing in the sand with its bill, it can tell immediately whether it is an inedible pebble or a tasty morsel worth eating.

MOVE-A-BILL

A number of bird species are able to bend sections of their bill. The special term for this is 'rhynchokinesis', from the Greek word meaning 'moving snout'. In snipes, for example, both the upper and lower parts of the bill are able to bend along their lengths. When the bird detects prey, the end of the upper mandible bends slightly upwards, allowing the tip of the bill to open. By sequentially opening and closing adjacent sections of its bill, the snipe is able to shift its prey along the length of the bill and into its mouth – all without needing to open the bill along its entire length or remove it from the mud.

The African Snipe can manoeuvre food to its mouth without fully opening its bill.

Examples of birds that hunt by touch alone are the Yellow-billed Stork, African Spoonbill, African Skimmer and Pied Avocet, and many other storks and waders. The Yellow-billed Stork wades slowly in shallow water, stirring the muddy bottom with its feet and snapping up any aquatic life that ventures within reach of its sensitive bill. The African Spoonbill rhythmically sweeps its slightly open bill from side to side, grabbing any prey felt between its mandibles. The African Skimmer has an exceptional bill, in that the lower mandible is longer than the upper. The bird flies back and forth low over the water surface, its sensitive lower bill scything the water and snapping shut as soon as it detects a fish.

The subtleties of smell

Compared to their vision and hearing, relatively little is known about how important the sense of smell is to birds. However, given that birds' olfactory bulbs – that part of the brain responsible for the sense of smell – are very small relative to those of similar-sized mammals, it is likely that their sense of smell is generally poor, and that they are not as dependent on smell for their survival as mammals are. The acuteness of this sense is thought to vary greatly between species, with some having a much keener sense of smell than others.

Petrels, such as this Pintado Petrel, are able to locate food through smell alone.

Honeyguides, such as this Greater Honeyguide, relish honeycombs and are thought to be attracted by the smell of wax. This was first noted as early as the 16th century by a Dominican missionary in Mozambique, who noticed that honeyguides were eating wax from the altar candles.

The role of smell in finding food

Although using their sense of smell for foraging is unusual in birds, it is thought to be important in certain species. In these birds, the olfactory bulb is large relative to the overall brain size.

In the open ocean, many pelagic species, especially the tube-nosed birds such as shearwaters, petrels and albatrosses, are able to detect and home in on food, based on its smell alone. They follow odour trails that are blown across the ocean surface with the wind and usually lead them to a valuable food source. Storm-petrels are able to detect these food sources from as far as 8 km away. The raised nostrils of the aptly named tube-nosed birds are unusual in that they open at the tip of the beak, rather than the base, as in most birds. They also have a **specialized olfactory system** inside the nasal cavity, which has a very large surface area that is highly sensitive to smell.

Communicating through smell

Most bird species have a range of different secretory glands throughout the body, from the preen gland at the base of the tail, which secretes an oily substance for feather care, to salivary glands in the mouth, and other glands in the skin and eyes.

It is well known that scent is a vital form of communication in mammals, used to recognize mates and family members, as part of courtship rituals, to mark territories and for self-defence. It is possible that birds, too, may use scent from their various secretory glands for similar purposes. This phenomenon has yet to be researched more thoroughly, however.

Shearwaters and petrels, which nest colonially in burrows, have good night vision and an acute sense of smell, which helps them to find their own nest sites in the dark – an essential ability, as they are active at night and regularly return to their nests under cover of darkness when they are safer from predators.

4 THE BREEDING GAME

A bustling colony of Cape Gannets

THE MOST PIVOTAL EVENT IN THE LIFE OF ANY BIRD IS THE ACT OF BREEDING since this allows each individual the important opportunity to pass its genes on to the next generation. For this reason, it is a time of frenetic activity where impassioned displays, fervent singing and hot-blooded threats all form part of the zealous competition for mates and territories.

While some birds show extreme loyalty to their partners and mate for life, others choose a new mate every breeding season. In some species, the males are blatantly promiscuous, attracting an entire harem of females each season, mating with and then abandoning them to brood and rear the young alone. In other species, breeding is a family affair, and not the job of just the biological parents alone: the whole extended family group co-operates and works together to rear the brood.

COURTSHIP RITUALS AND MATING

In a number of species, male birds have clearly mastered the art of courtship, using a range of methods to attract and win over females. The male's striking plumage and distinctive songs often act as triggers for the female to come into breeding condition. In colonial species, courtship displays by just a few birds may, in fact, result in a domino effect, stimulating the rest of the colony members into breeding mode as well. Song is an integral part of courtship behaviour. (For more information on this, see Chapter 9, Songs and Sounds.)

Mating displays

Many species use elaborate courtship behaviour to catch the eye of potential mates, from impressive and animated displays, to flaunting their bright, attractive colours and showcasing their melodious songs.

A good example is the Red-crested Korhaan, appropriately known as the 'suicide bird'. The male is well known for its dramatic habit of flying high into the air, then plummeting to the ground like a meteorite falling from the sky, veering away to the side in daredevil fashion at the last moment. Bishops are renowned for their bright breeding plumage combined with their conspicuous and frenetic 'bumble-bee' flight as they display with zeal over their territories. The Lilac-breasted Roller is appropriately named after its distinctive aerial rolling display, in which it tumbles through the sky in a dramatic looping flight. However, it is not always just the male who performs. In many species, both birds display together.

The male Paradise Whydah uses its elaborate tail in courtship displays.

The male Kori Bustard displays to the female with neck inflated, tail raised over its back and undertail coverts fanned.

Blue Cranes often perform elegant display dances during courtship.

The pair bond

Once birds have assessed and chosen their breeding partners, a pair bond forms that needs to be nurtured and maintained. While most birds pair up for the breeding season only and the pair bond does not survive beyond this period, several long-lived species such as some cranes, eagles, albatrosses, geese and swans show a more long-term commitment by mating for life. Among these devoted couples, a 'divorce' occurs only rarely, and then usually because the union has failed to result in successful breeding.

Whether the pair bond lasts a season or a lifetime, it may be maintained and strengthened by a range of behaviours, from impassioned ritual greetings and songs, to generous 'nuptial gifts' and allopreening.

Nuptial gifts

When it comes to choosing a mate, the well-known adage could aptly be changed to 'the route to a *female's* heart is through her stomach', as many male birds bring gifts of food to the female as part of the courtship ritual. Since a regular food supply is so important to

WOOING WEAVERS

The weavers are unusual in that, unlike most birds, they use their intricately woven nests as a showpiece to attract their mates. When the male has completed his nest he hangs upside down from the entrance and displays vigorously to passing females by singing persistently, and flapping his wings. Females will stop to inspect the range of options on the 'property market', and each will choose the male that, in her eyes, is the most accomplished and skillful builder. The criteria that the critical female uses to select the nest hinge on the strength and firmness of the weave, as these will ensure the most secure shelter for her offspring. The female completes the nest by lining it with soft material so that it is ready for her to lay her eggs.

A male Village Weaver hangs from its nest entrance displaying to the female, calling and shaking its wings agitatedly.

A male Rufous-naped lark offers a female a 'nuptial gift'.

usually preen feathers that the other bird cannot reach itself, such as those on the head and neck. This is a type of mutual 'I'll scratch your back if you'll scratch mine' arrangement. Over and above the practical benefits of helping to clean plumage and remove parasites, allopreening is thought to be even more important in strengthening and cementing the pair bond.

GENDER DIFFERENCES

In many bird species the male differs greatly in appearance from the female, usually being brighter in colour and more striking than his mate. This is known as **sexual dimorphism**.

In some species this gender difference lasts only for the duration of the breeding season when males need to flaunt their striking breeding plumage in order to attract females. While being an advantage during the breeding season, this conspicuous mating attire can be a disadvantage in other ways as bright colours make birds

birds, especially during the breeding season, it is thought that, in certain species, the female chooses a male that will best be able to provide for her and her chicks. Courtship feeding could be a good indicator of this ability. Some male terns are known to advertise their availability at the beginning of the breeding season by flying over the nesting ground with fish in their beaks. In many species, the male continues to bring food to the female during incubation, after which he also helps to feed the newly hatched chicks. Rather than just providing nourishment for the female, however, it is thought that these so-called 'nuptial gifts' are an important means of helping to strengthen the pair bond. Courtship feeding is found in many species, from dabchicks, kingfishers and bee-eaters, to raptors, finches and larks.

Affectionate allopreening

Another interesting form of courtship behaviour is allopreening, where birds preen the plumage of their mates. They

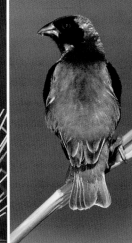

Male Southern Red Bishops have striking breeding plumage (RIGHT) compared to their drab, non-breeding eclipse or 'out-of-season' plumage (LEFT).

more noticeable to predators, while long tails can impede their flight. These birds therefore moult out of their feathered finery and into more drab plumage (known as 'eclipse plumage') until the next breeding season. Examples of such birds include bishops, weavers, whydahs, widowbirds and many waders.

In other species, the male and female retain their different appearances throughout the year. For example, the male Saddle-billed Stork has yellow wattles at the base of his bill and a brown eye compared to the bright yellow eye of the wattle-less female. In some sunbirds, the males are feathered in bright colours and shimmering hues, while the less flashy females have dull plumage. A subtle yet distinct difference between male and female Bateleurs can be seen in their wing patterning – the male having a broader black band on its underwing than the female. In general, raptors challenge the gender stereotype: in contrast to most birds, females are usually much bigger than the males; this is known as 'reverse sexual dimorphism'.

The male Saddle-billed Stork (RIGHT) has yellow wattles and brown eyes; the female is wattle-less and has bright yellow eyes (LEFT).

PASSIONATE PARTNERSHIPS

As in human society, birds form many different kinds of partnerships during the breeding season, ranging from life-long commitments and the sharing of parental duties, to nothing more than brief, promiscuous matings. However, irrespective of the kind of partnership, the goal is invariably the same: that of producing the greatest number of offspring.

Monogamy: faithful to one partner

The majority of birds are monogamous (Greek: *monus*, single; *gamos*, marriage), with breeding partnerships in about 90 per cent of all species being between a single male and a single female. Depending on the species, this monogamous partnership can last for either one breeding cycle or for an entire lifetime, with both male and female usually sharing either all or most of the parental duties. For birds that stay with the same partner for a long period of time, choosing the best mate is particularly important.

In order to guarantee his paternity, the male bird needs to make sure that other males do not mate with his female, since he would be wasting valuable time and energy if he happened to raise offspring that were not his own. In order to do this, the male often guards his mate protectively, as well as vigorously defending his territory by singing and displaying. Having said this, casual 'affairs' between the male and other females are not altogether unusual. Male birds are invariably opportunistic and, if given the chance, will not always pass up the option of mating with other available females.

The male Pin-tailed Whydah displays vigorously to the drab female.

Polygyny: promiscuous partnerships

Polygyny (Greek: *poly*, many; *gyna*, woman) occurs when one male pairs with a number of different females, and is found in about 10 per cent of bird species.

Polygynous males invest as little of their time and energy into parental care as possible, and these avian 'chauvinists' usually leave the responsibility of incubating the eggs and raising the chicks to the female. This gives them more time to attract and mate with other females and sire more offspring per breeding season. Their contribution usually goes little further than fertilizing the female and possibly nest-building, and no lasting bond between the pair is formed. Some males do, however, spend much energy defending their harems from other males, as can be seen among weavers and widowbirds.

To attract females, polygynous males usually have attractive feather colour and ornate and elaborate tails compared to the drabber females (*see* Gender differences, page 58).

Polyandry: feathered feminism

Polyandry (Greek: *poly*, many; *andros*, man) is a highly unusual mating system in which a female pairs with several different males, and is therefore the opposite of polygyny. This reversal of traditional sex roles is very

In African Jacanas the male is smaller than the female and raises the brood.

FLIGHTS OF FANCY

The male Long-tailed Widowbird is well known for flaunting its extremely long, elaborate tail as it ardently displays around its territory. It has been shown that in the case of tail length, size *does* count, with longer tails being more attractive to passing females. One possible explanation for the widowbird's *excessively* long tail is thought to be the 'runaway hypothesis'. This theory states that, because females select males based on tail length, males with longer tails father more offspring, including females who select for long tails, and so the cycle continues.

Another explanation for long tails, linked to the 'runaway hypothesis', is that of the 'handicap principle'. This theory states that there comes a point when the extra-long tail, although an advantage to the male for attracting females, in fact starts to become a cumbersome handicap, as it hinders the bird during feeding and escaping from predators. However, the fact that the male bird has such a handicap and yet still manages to survive and thrive, is an additional sign to females of his superior fitness. They are therefore more likely to favour these males when choosing a mate.

The male Long-tailed Widowbird flaunts an impressive tail during the breeding season.

rare in birds, and occurs in fewer than one per cent of all species. The female bird, having laid one clutch, abandons these eggs along with the father in order to seek out another male to fertilize her next clutch, leaving the initial male to take on all the parental duties, from incubating the eggs to raising and defending the chicks. Polyandrous birds are also unusual in that the females are usually larger and may be more brightly coloured than the males – an example of reverse sexual dimorphism (*see* page 58).

In southern Africa, the African Jacana and Greater Painted-Snipe are well known examples of polyandrous species. While in both species the female is larger than the male, the female Greater Painted-Snipe is also more strikingly coloured. The Lesser Jacana, in contrast, is monogamous.

LEK DISPLAYS

In certain highly promiscuous birds, the fierce rivalry between males for females takes place at traditional display grounds known as 'leks' (from the Scandinavian word meaning 'play'). Although lekking systems are uncommon among southern African birds, the Ruff, which does not breed but over-winters in southern Africa, is a typical example of a lekking species. On their northern breeding grounds, these male birds live up to their name and develop a magnificent ruff of feathers around their necks. They gather together at lek sites to display competitively and show off their finery. Within the lek, each male occupies a small area known as a 'court'. The leks are visited by female Ruffs (called 'Reeves') who assess the desirability and 'fitness' of the impassioned displaying birds, and choose to mate with the dominant cocks. Among the southern African birds, group displays of whydahs represent the closest version of such a lekking system.

CO-OPERATIVE BREEDERS

In many species, breeding pairs do not raise their chicks alone, but are helped by other birds in their flock. These helpful 'nannies' may take on a range of different duties, from nest-building and bringing food to the hungry chicks, to sharing in incubation and defending the brood against predators. Having these devoted baby-sitters has been shown to greatly increase the chances of the chicks surviving to adulthood.

One might question why other birds should assist in this way, rather than putting their time and effort into raising broods of their own. In most cases, the helpers are related to the breeding pair, often their offspring from a previous brood. In this situation, there is an advantage in helping, as they share much of their genetic make-up with the new brood. They are not, therefore, being completely altruistic since they are in effect ensuring that some of their own genes are passed on to the next generation. This is known as 'kin-selection'.

Another possible explanation for co-operative breeding is that, by foraging and roosting together in groups, birds are less vulnerable to predators, as the collective eyes of the group are more likely to detect any danger. This makes living co-operatively an advantage even during the non-breeding season. By acting as helpers, young birds are also thought to gain valuable experience in chick-raising that they can later use when raising their own offspring.

Green Wood-Hoopoes are well known for their co-operative breeding habits.

Whether to help or not

Bird species that breed co-operatively are split into two groups: 'obligate' co-operative breeders always breed together, while 'facultative' co-operative breeders breed as a group only under certain circumstances.

Obligate co-operative breeders usually live in so-called 'stable' habitats where there is a constant food supply that can support birds living in groups throughout the year. Arrow-marked Babblers, Pied Kingfishers, White-crested and Retz's Helmet-Shrikes, oxpeckers, some bee-eaters and Southern Ground-Hornbills fall into this group.

By contrast, facultative co-operative breeders breed together only when the benefits are greater than those of breeding alone. Species such as the Southern Pale Chanting Goshawk and Violet-backed Starling sometimes breed together, but not invariably so. These birds usually live in habitats that are not stable, and, because food supplies may vary and sometimes be limited, it is difficult for groups of birds to remain together in permanent territories. Co-operative breeding under these conditions is unpredictable from year to year, and only occurs when there are unfavourable environmental conditions. Other examples of facultative co-operative breeders include the Hamerkop, moorhens, African Hoopoe and Cape Wagtail.

OSTRICHES: PUTTING ALL THEIR EGGS INTO ONE BASKET

The Common Ostrich's rather complicated mating habits make it difficult to classify as either completely monogamous or completely polygynous. Male ostriches defend large territories within which they may court a number of females, eventually settling on one dominant hen, called the major hen, to 'rule the roost'. She lays her eggs in a nest scrape on the ground. The other subordinate or minor hens with which the male has mated, add their eggs to her nest.

Although the major hen allows this, only she and the male actually incubate the eggs. Because it is often impossible for one bird to cover all the eggs if the clutch is large, the minor hens' eggs are often pushed to the edge of the nest. It is thought that the major hen is able

A female Common Ostrich sitting on her nest by day; the male tends the eggs at night.

to distinguish her own eggs from those of the other females (possibly by the pore patterns on the shell). In so doing, she creates a buffer against predators since the eggs on the edge of the nest are more likely to be taken, and this reduces the chances of her own eggs being eaten. Although this does not seem like a fair deal for the minor hens, the consolation is that there is still a chance that some of their eggs will survive to hatch, and will be looked after by the major hen.

5 NESTS AND NESTING

THE AVIAN 'PROPERTY MARKET' IS AS VARIED AS THE HUMAN ONE, ranging from 'penthouses' to 'huts'. The majestic Secretarybird values a panoramic view, and builds its huge nest platform in the canopy of a large tree with a vista overlooking the open plains. In contrast, the Cape Robin-Chat prefers a more secluded location, siting its delicate, cup-shaped nest in the privacy of a thick bush. Large, congested colonies of herons and egrets, with nests like clustered urban townhouses, are found in trees above dams, while the floating houseboat-like nests of the Little Grebe and Red-knobbed Coot lie moored on the water below. Some eagles build huge nests or 'eyries' positioned on dramatic vertical cliff-faces like high-rise skyscrapers. And nightjars, rather than building an elaborate mansion like that of the Hamerkop, build no nest at all, preferring to 'camp' in the open and lay their eggs on the ground.

Chinspot Batis in
a cup-shaped nest

The typical cup-shaped nest of the African Paradise Flycatcher

RANGE OF BIRD REAL ESTATE

Many birds are accomplished architects and builders, and, just as we use a wide range of materials to build our homes, so too do birds use an astonishing diversity of nesting materials to build theirs. These range from leaves, grasses, twigs and reeds to spider webs, lichen, feathers, mud and saliva, while some birds even make use of man-made materials such as wire, glass, cotton, string, and cement in their nest construction. When looking at the impressive range of nest designs and the innovative yet functional use of nesting materials, one can only stand back and admire the ingenuity and skill of these avian architects.

It is useful to classify avian 'real estate' into categories based on nest type and materials used.

Classical cup-shapes

Many of the smaller birds build open, cup-shaped nests. These are usually concealed in the branches of a tree, with coarser material used for the framework and finer material lining the 'cup'. Although each nest is unique and characteristic of a particular species, this basic cup-shaped structure is the most common nest type and is used by as many as 200 bird species in southern Africa. Birds that build this type of nest include buntings, canaries, white-eyes, shrikes, robin-chats, thrushes, bulbuls, babblers, drongos and mousebirds.

Woven balls

The next most common design after the cup shape is that of an enclosed, ball-shaped structure with an entrance either at the side or underneath. This nest type is used by about 130 species in southern Africa and, although typical of weavers, also includes the sunbirds, coucals, bishops, sparrows, queleas, cisticolas and many warblers. Although many of these species nest alone, some of the weavers set up home in colonies, while the highly gregarious quelea nests alongside hundreds to thousands of other birds.

The woven, ball-shaped nest of the Marico Sunbird

The small, saucer-shaped stick platform of the Namaqua Dove

The large, saucer-shaped stick platform of the Verreauxs' Eagle

Saucers of sticks

These nests are made of sticks and twigs, and range from small to large platforms. The former are generally simple, fragile-looking, saucer-shaped structures made of twigs and plant stems, and are used by pigeons, doves and turacos. By contrast, many other species build larger, more robust stick platforms in trees, usually in forks or on horizontal branches. A heronry is a good example of such nests, where hundreds of birds may build individual nests together in large colonies, usually in big trees surrounded by a protective moat of water. Besides herons and egrets, these colonies may comprise a mix of different species such as cormorants, African Darters, Sacred Ibises and African Spoonbills. Many raptors and storks also build large stick platforms in tree-tops, which are often surprisingly well concealed despite their impressive size.

A FRESH, GREEN LINING

A leaf-lined nest of Wahlberg's Eagle

After completing their large platform nests, many eagles line their nests with a thick layer of green leaves, which they continually replenish with new leaves as incubation proceeds. Although the reason for this habit is somewhat of a mystery, a number of theories have been put forward. It could be that the aromatic leaves of some plants help to repel parasites. The leafy layer could help to block up the gaps between the sticks, and so help to insulate the nest from air draughts. It may also help to keep the nest area hygienic by preventing pieces of food from falling out of reach into the spaces between the twigs, and decaying there.

Mud shelters

Swallows and martins are among the most specialized builders, constructing their nests almost entirely of mud. The mud pellets are collected from the edges of pools, and, when dry, form hard, cement-like walls. Grass is sometimes mixed with the mud to make a strong mortar. Mud-pellet nests can be divided into three types: open, cup-shaped nests (that of the Pearl-breasted Swallow, for example), closed bowls with or without a short side entrance (the Mosque Swallow) and closed bowls with a long entrance tunnel (the Lesser Striped Swallow). Many species attach their nests to a man-made structure, such as the eaves of a house roof or the underside of a bridge. These hardy mud shelters are often re-used year after year.

The impressive, bulky stick mansion of the Hamerkop

Many swallows build their nests entirely from mud. Pictured here is the nest of a Greater Striped Swallow.

Stick mansions

The Hamerkop's **gigantic, dome-shaped mansion** is made with literally thousands of sticks, as well as grass, leaves, weeds and an eclectic range of miscellaneous human debris such as plastic, cloth, wire and string. In fact, anything interesting that they can get their beaks on may find its way into the nest construction. It is estimated that some 8 000 pieces of material can be used to

Some birds, such as this Verreaux's Eagle-Owl, make free use of the Hamerkop's nest once it has been deserted by its former owners.

make one nest. The entrance tunnel leads into a central chamber in which the birds lay their eggs and incubate their young. The walls and floor are plastered with mud, which acts to insulate and waterproof the chamber. The nest is usually built high up in the fork of a large tree, but also occasionally on rock ledges. It is often used by other bird species such as owls, kestrels and ducks, as well as by bees, snakes and genets, and is sometimes appropriated even before the Hamerkops themselves have begun to breed! Similar, but much smaller, dome-shaped nests are made by the Wattled Starling and the Red-billed Buffalo-Weaver.

Sociable Weavers are famous for building the **largest nests in the world**, which can reach 7 m in diameter, 4 m in height and can weigh nearly a ton, sometimes breaking the boughs of large trees. These giant grassy communes can have a phenomenal lifespan of over 100 years, spanning many successive generations, and can accommodate up to 500 birds at one time. The nests are built to regulate temperature, keeping the air cool during extremely hot summer days and warmer than the freezing outside temperatures in winter. Other bird tenants that use empty chambers in the nests include Pygmy

Sociable Weavers hold the record for building the largest nests in the world.

SILKY STRENGTH

Many birds, such as flycatchers, sunbirds, batises and shrikes, use spider web as a flexible binding material to strengthen their nests. Spider web is a prime choice of building material, given that it is known to be one of the strongest natural materials in the world.

The nest of the White-crested Helmet-shrike is bound together with spider silk.

Falcons (whose presence may be detected by the ring of white droppings around the entrance), Red-headed Finches, Rosy-faced Lovebirds and Acacia Pied Barbets. Larger birds such as Secretarybirds and owls may nest on the roof of the mound once the nest has been deserted.

Skyscrapers

Birds that nest on skyscraper-like cliffs include the solitary Verreauxs' and Booted eagles, Augur and Jackal buzzards and White-necked Ravens. Some cliff-nesters such as the Southern Bald Ibis and the Cape Vulture nest in extensive colonies. Nesting on relatively inaccessible cliffs provides good security and, in the case of raptors, aids in spotting prey. Many species return year after year to the same breeding sites. A pair of Verreauxs' Eagles may use the same nest for over a decade. Nest sites can often be identified from a distance by the distinctive 'whitewashing' of the cliffs below, which is caused by defecation.

'Camping' in the open

Some birds, such as lapwings, bustards, terns and night-jars, nest on the open ground, using little or no nesting material, since building a nest would make them more conspicuous. Most of these birds rely on exceptional camouflage, and the eggs and chicks blend perfectly with the ground. In some species, such as nightjars, the eggs are laid directly on the undisturbed ground, while in others a shallow scrape is made. Certain species, such as the arid-zone larks, add materials such as grass, small stones and even animal droppings to the scrape. Many birds breeding in freshwater or coastal habitats camp in the open air, but use some sort of material to line their ground nests. Most of the ducks and geese use their own plucked down feathers, while Cape and Bank cormorants line their nests with seaweed, feathers and debris washed up along the coast.

Most nightjars lay their eggs on the open ground, relying on camouflage to keep them safe from predators.

Verreauxs' Eagles are known to use the same nest site for more than a decade.

The Red-knobbed Coot builds its floating nest with aquatic plants.

Avian houseboats

Birds such as jacanas, grebes and the Red-knobbed Coot build their nests on water. These houseboat-like nests are constructed from aquatic plants and are able to float on the water. Sometimes they are anchored, which makes them more susceptible to flooding than free-floating nests. Eggs are often covered with nesting material before being left unattended.

Hollowed-out homes

While some birds chisel, scrape or dig their hollowed-out homes into sandy banks or tree trunks, others do not excavate the holes themselves but rather use natural holes in trees or the holes made and vacated by other birds or even other animals.

Most species that nest in **holes in banks**, such as bee-eaters, kingfishers and martins, excavate these tunnels for themselves. However,

Besides using their beaks to dig, bee-eaters also use their beaks and wings as a tripod. This frees their legs to dig, kick and clear soil from the burrow.

Southern Carmine Bee-eaters nest communally in holes in a sandy bank.

some tunnel-nesters prefer to use holes dug by other birds. The Capped Wheatear uses rodent holes as nest sites. The South African Shelduck, some bee-eaters and the endangered Blue Swallow nest underground, often in disused aardvark holes.

／ Birds with suitably strong, hardy bills such as woodpeckers, barbets and tinkerbirds are able to excavate their own **nest holes**, usually in **dead trees**. The circular entrances are typically just wide enough for the parent bird to enter. Most of these species excavate a new nest hole each year. Barbets are unusual in that they often use these holes to roost in at night outside the breeding season.

Barn Owls often make use of existing tree cavities as nest sites.

The Crested Barbet usually nests in a self-excavated hole in a dead tree.

／ Many birds make use of **natural tree holes** as nesting sites. These holes may be caused by lightning strikes, wood rot or branches breaking off, or excavation by species such as barbets and woodpeckers. Birds using this form of hollowed-out home include oxpeckers, starlings, tits, hornbills, parrots, lovebirds, hoopoes, rollers and many owls.

SEALED IN

Most hornbills construct their nests in natural tree holes, and their nesting habits have an unusual twist. Once a suitable hole is selected, the female seals herself in with mud provided by the male, often strengthened with a mixture of her own faeces as well as nest debris and insect remains. This hard plug serves as a good predator deterrent and helps prevent nest take-overs by other hole-nesting birds. The female lays her clutch and incubates the eggs, all the while being fed by the male through a narrow slit. She even pushes out her moulted feathers, and defecates, through the slit. Once the chicks have hatched and are old enough to accept food, the female breaks out of the nest and the entrance is re-sealed by the chicks. The adults then feed the young through the opening until they fledge.

Unique nests

The architectural design and building style of the nests of some species are so exceptional that they deserve special mention.

▌ Swifts have a problem when it comes to gathering nesting material, as their feet are so small and weak that they cannot land to pick up material from the ground as other birds do (*see page 18*). Instead, they gather feathers, pieces of dried grass and other material adrift in the air. They then draw on a unique, self-made binding material to construct the nest: vast quantities of their own **sticky saliva, which hardens when dry.** This is produced from salivary glands that become particularly enlarged in the breeding season. The African Palm-Swift takes this further by also gluing its eggs to its precarious hanging nest, attached to a palm leaf, so that they don't fall out. In southeast Asia, the hardened saliva nests of the Edible-nest Swiftlets are regarded as a culinary delicacy.

The African Palm-Swift's nest is bound by its sticky saliva.

Another unique nest design is that of the **Cape Penduline-Tit**. The **oval-shaped bag** has a felt-like appearance, being closely knitted together using soft materials such as plant fibres, sheep's wool and spider web. Its entrance is near the top of the nest, and has a flap that can be opened and closed as the bird enters and leaves. There is a convenient platform just below this entrance on which the bird perches before entering the nest to incubate its eggs or feed its young. Above the platform, a hollowed-out indentation gives the appearance of being the true nest entrance; this 'false entrance' is thought to act as a decoy or defence against marauding predators.

Crombecs build a distinctive, **purse-like nest** that they suspend from the end of a branch. Various materials are used to build the nest, including grass, small sticks and bark, which are bound to the branch with strong spider web. The nest is then camouflaged with leaves, lichen, flakes of wood and even caterpillar droppings. Crombecs are known to use the same nest site year after year.

The unusual purse-like nest of the Long-billed Crombec

true entrance

false entrance

The unique felt-like nest of the Cape Penduline-Tit with its distinctive 'false entrance'

WEAVING WIZARDRY

Weavers are renowned for being among the most accomplished weaving wizards of the bird world, with nests that are intricately and skillfully woven. Each weaver species has specialized in a unique nest-making 'formula', and is able to create nests of a distinctive shape and size.

Design diversity

The nests of different weaver species can be broadly classified according to the position and length of their entrance tunnels. It is thought that nest structures with long entrance spouts have evolved more recently than those with shorter spouts, since a longer spout is thought to be more effective in combating predation.

Weaver nests come in four main designs:

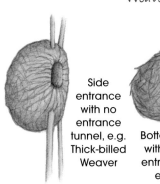

Side entrance with no entrance tunnel, e.g. Thick-billed Weaver

Bottom entrance with short or no entrance tunnel, e.g. Village Weaver

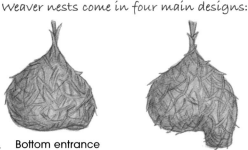

Bottom entrance with short entrance tunnel, e.g. Lesser Masked-Weaver

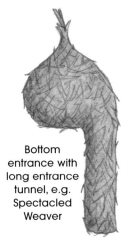

Bottom entrance with long entrance tunnel, e.g. Spectacled Weaver

Different weaves

The weavers have developed and perfected their nest-making technique by evolving a range of different stitches, some to construct the nest itself, and others to attach the nest securely to either a branch or to reeds. They wield their beaks and feet much as we would a needle to stitch thread.

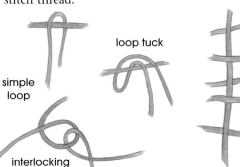

simple loop

loop tuck

interlocking loops

simple weave

half hitch

spiral coil

alternately revised winding

Weavers use a variety of 'stitches' to construct and attach their woven nests.

Ref. Collias, N.E. and Collias, E.C. 1984. Nest Building and Bird Behaviour. Princeton University Press, New Jersey.

The weaving process

Male weavers follow a number of distinct steps in weaving their nests. After securing the initial attachment to a suitable branch, the weaver builds the ring – the foundation of the nest. Next, the roof is woven over the top of the ring, followed by the bulbous egg chamber. The ante-chamber, which serves as the foyer of the home, and the entrance to the nest are then completed, followed lastly by the entrance tunnel (in those species where this structure is built). In some species, the tunnel is added only after the female has approved the nest.

Once the female has critically inspected the male's handiwork and given her approval of the nest, she adds the finishing touches by providing a layer of soft, thick lining to the egg chamber.

The woven nest of the Lesser Masked-Weaver

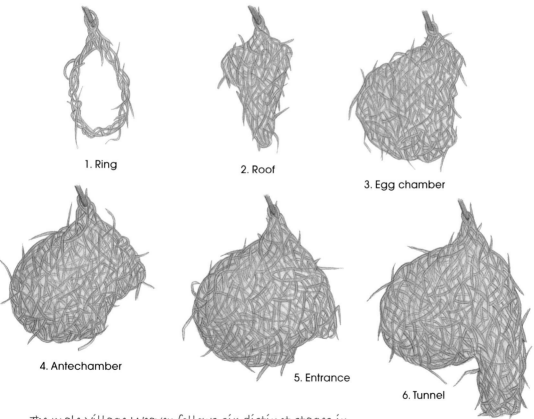

1. Ring

2. Roof

3. Egg chamber

4. Antechamber

5. Entrance

6. Tunnel

The male Village Weaver follows six distinct stages in constructing his woven nest.

IS NEST-BUILDING INNATE OR LEARNED?

How do young birds breeding for the first time automatically know how to build their often complex nests? Research has shown that the nest-building skill seems to be largely instinctive. For example, male Village Weavers hand-raised in totally artificial conditions, and without ever having seen a nest, are still able to build a passable nest.

However, it is thought that this skill is refined and improved on by a process of trial and error gained through experience. While a young bird's first attempt at nest-building is often unskilled, its efforts improve greatly with practice and as it becomes more skilled at choosing the right materials and perfecting its weaving technique. This learning process is particularly important in species that build elaborate nests, such as the weavers, which refine their weaving and knot-tying abilities the more they practise.

In many species, young chicks imprint on the position of their nest site, as well as the materials used to construct the nest, and they are thought to draw on this knowledge when they reach maturity and start nesting themselves.

The Red-headed Weaver uses dry twigs and leaves.

The Thick-billed Weaver uses thin strips of reeds.

The Southern Masked-Weaver uses thicker strips of grass and leaves.

Pliable plants

Each weaver species makes use of slightly different materials. These can range from the dry twigs and leaves used by the Red-headed Weaver, and the neatly woven, thin strips of grass and reeds in the case of the Thick-billed Weaver, to the thicker grass and leaves used by the Southern Masked-Weaver. An interesting feature of many weavers is the male's habit of stripping off all the foliage from the branches or reeds surrounding the nests. This is thought to make the nests more visible to passing females.

'LOCATION, LOCATION, LOCATION'

The estate agents' axiom that the three most important factors affecting property value are 'location, location and location' applies, to a large extent, in the weaver world too, where different species nest in very different locations, depending on their particular habits.

Reedbeds are the preferred location of the Thick-billed, Southern Brown-throated, Golden and Yellow weavers, which all attach their nests to upright reed stalks. The Village, Lesser Masked and Cape weavers also choose to nest near water, but suspend their nests from the canopies of large trees (particularly acacias). Spectacled Weavers usually nest in riparian forests alongside flowing rivers, while the Dark-backed Weaver locates its nest in thick primary or secondary forests. The Red-headed Weaver prefers nesting in bushveld habitats, while the Southern Masked-Weaver may breed in a number of different habitats, from gardens to savannah woodlands.

WHY BUILD A NEST?

Contrary to what is often thought, birds do not build nests primarily to sleep in at night, but rather for the important purpose of breeding.

A secure nursery

The main function of the nest is to provide a safe home environment for the developing eggs and growing chicks. The nest allows for constant, controlled conditions, offering the eggs, and later, the chicks, protection against bad weather conditions. The materials used to build the nest often help insulate the eggs and keep them warm while the parent is away.

Escaping predators

Birds have had to evolve strategies to escape from predators such as mongooses, genets and servals, boomslangs and egg-eaters, and avian attackers such as the African Harrier-Hawk and sparrowhawks.

One way to outsmart predators is for birds to render their nests close to invisible, using various **means of camouflage**. The Chinspot Batis, for example, covers its nest with a layer of mottled lichen, blending the nest in so perfectly with the branch on which it is placed that it is almost undetectable. Ground-nesting birds such as plovers, coursers, pipits and larks are also masters of camouflage, laying eggs that so closely match the surrounding ground that one almost treads on them before noticing them. This deception is further aided by the camouflage colour of the adult birds incubating on the nest. Some bird species such as francolins disguise their clutch by hiding their nest in thick vegetation, while others use a closed nest in which their eggs are hidden.

FEATHERED CARGO PLANES

The female Rosy-faced Lovebird uses a very unusual method of transporting nesting material to her nest: she tucks strips of leaves, grass and bark into the feathers on her lower back and rump. These specially adapted contour feathers have tiny hooks that link adjacent feathers together, holding the material lodged between them and preventing it from falling out during flight. By contrast, Lilian's and Black-cheeked lovebirds use the more conventional method – their beaks – to carry nesting material.

The Rosy-faced Lovebird carries its nesting material between the feathers on its rump.

The male Cape Weaver gathers material for its nest.

Various bird species build their **nests in inaccessible places** in order to escape predators. Many swallows and swifts, for example, nest under bridges or cliff faces, while waterbirds tend to build their nests in trees surrounded by a moat of water or in thick reedbeds. Red-billed Buffalo-Weavers and Cape Sparrows often build their nests in impenetrable acacia trees, protected from predators by the sharp thorns.

Species that construct enclosed nests, such as weavers and sunbirds, can rely on **thick, strong walls** to prevent predators from reaching their eggs or chicks.

Some birds, such as the House Sparrow and White Stork, often nest near **human habitation**, presumably benefiting from fewer incidents of predation. Other birds choose to associate with formidable non-avian species for protection. The Blue Waxbill and various weavers are known to build their nests close to wasp colonies, an effective means of deterring potential predators.

WHO BUILDS THE NEST?

Depending on the species, building the nest can be the task of both male and female working together, or just one of the pair.

Sharing the workload

In many birds, both sexes share the workload. It is thought that building together strengthens the pair bond, and makes it more likely that the male will also help to incubate the eggs and feed the chicks. Some eagle species are good examples of this, as are some of the swallows and waxbills.

Where both male and female share nest building, they sometimes have different roles. In species such as herons, doves and pigeons, the male gathers the material and brings it to the nest site, while the female actually constructs the nest. Among weavers and widowbirds, the male builds the outer shell of the nest, leaving the female to add the inner lining.

Single-parent home

In species such as sunbirds and sugarbirds, as well as many robin-chats and thrushes, the female takes on the building task alone. She may also incubate alone, although the male usually helps to feed the ever-hungry chicks once they hatch. In rare cases such as the African Jacana, the male takes on all parental duties, and is left to build the nest and incubate the eggs alone (*see also* page 61).

Opportunistic tenants

Some birds take the easy option when it comes to establishing a home. Rather than building their own nest, they take advantage of the efforts of others. For example, the enormous Sociable Weaver nest may accommodate a variety of different 'tenants' from Acacia Pied Barbets to Barn Owls and Pygmy Falcons. Verreaux's Eagle-Owls often take over old Hamerkop nests, while Orange-breasted Waxbills and Red-headed and Cut-throat finches may make their homes in old Southern Red Bishop nests. Grey-headed Sparrows and Mocking Cliff-Chats regularly nest in old swallow nests.

The Southern Grey-headed Sparrow raises its brood in a deserted swallow's nest.

BIRDS THAT RE-USE THEIR NESTS

Usually a nest is used once only, after which it is abandoned and a new nest built the following breeding season. Exceptions to this are many raptors, the Hamerkop, the Secretarybird and the Sociable Weaver, which often use the same nest year after year, making improvements and renovations during each successive nesting cycle. The Lesser Striped Swallow is also known to return annually to precisely the same nesting site, while the Southern Ground-Hornbill has been known to use the same nest for decades.

Secretarybirds use the same nest year after year.

'BIRDS OF A FEATHER FLOCK TOGETHER'

Some birds nest alone in secluded locations, while others gather in huge, bustling, jostling colonies numbering literally thousands of birds, where neighbours are a mere beak-stab away. Most birds breed solitarily within a demarcated territory that provides them with all their needs. However, for colonial species, each 'territory' is reduced to the nest site itself and the immediate area around it, often just within pecking distance of the nearest neighbours.

Many waterbirds are colonial nesters, and colonies may consist of different species, such as herons, egrets, ibises, cormorants and spoonbills. Crowded colonies are also common among marine birds like gannets. The Cape Vulture is a well-known colonial species nesting on exposed cliffs, while many weavers, bishops, widowbirds, swallows and swifts also nest colonially. Nesting colonies are generally situated in safe sites, such as islands, cliffs, tall and isolated trees, very thorny trees, caves, buildings or vegetation over water.

Most colonies have what is known as a 'biological centre', with the safer and therefore more successful nest sites in the middle of the colony. Younger birds usually have to make do with the more hazardous peripheral sites and are less productive.

The colonial choice

As any estate agent knows, every position has its trade-offs, and colonial birds do sometimes experience disadvantages when nesting so closely together. Crowding often means that there is more competition for food and suitble nesting sites, and many birds losing out in this competition may fail to breed. Since birds make themselves more conspicuous by nesting in colonies, and also have to compete with so many

Cape Gannets nest in packed colonies.

others for nest sites, nesting materials and food, one may question the rationale for the practice. However, on closer examination, there are advantages to this highly sociable existence:

/ Where available **nesting space is limited**, such as on small offshore islands, birds have little option but to make the best possible use of the space by nesting closely together.

/ With the sharp eyes of the **many colony members on the lookout for danger**, there is little chance of a predator going unnoticed. Birds may also gang up to chase intruders away.

/ Being surrounded by hundreds of other birds reduces the individual's chance of having their eggs or chicks preyed upon. This **'swamping' effect** can be seen among Red-billed Queleas, which nest in their thousands, and so the chance of one particular individual being preyed upon is relatively small.

/ In colonial species, the amorous courtship displays of a few birds at the start of the breeding season are thought to **stimulate the rest of the colony into breeding mode.**

6 EXPLORING EGGS

APTLY DESCRIBED BY RENOWNED ORNITHOLOGIST ROBERT BURTON AS 'NATURE'S MIRACLE OF PACKAGING', birds' eggs come in an unexpected variety of shapes, with their colours, textures and patterns forming natural artworks on the calcium canvas of the shell.

While other groups of egg-laying vertebrates, such as reptiles and amphibians, have at least some species that give birth to live young, all birds are egg-laying. The main reason for this is that birds would become far too heavy to fly if they incubated their eggs inside their bodies. Carrying even a single egg until live birth would seriously impair a bird's flight; a whole clutch would, of course, be impossible. For birds, incubating their eggs outside their bodies is the only option.

The female Kurrichane Thrush would have taken three days to lay her entire clutch – each egg being laid 24 hours apart.

FORMATION OF THE EGG

It takes about 24 hours for the egg of a smallish bird to form, from the time that it is fertilized to the time that it is laid. Because only one egg can be produced at a time, birds can't lay their whole clutch in one sitting – eggs are laid at least 24 hours apart. The eggs of many larger birds, such as raptors, cranes, storks and ostriches, take longer to form, and the interval between laying consecutive eggs can be anything from two to five days.

Most birds are early-morning layers, which means that they don't have to carry the heavy egg with them while out foraging during the day. Also, it is thought that the best time for the formation of the delicate eggshell is at night when the mother is inactive, resting before her morning 'labour'.

Sperm to order

A bird's egg can be fertilized by sperm from a male that has mated with her in the previous few minutes. Alternatively, it can be fertilized by sperm stored by the female in her own internal 'sperm bank' – specialized tubules that can store sperm for days or even weeks before it is used. This means that sperm from one mating can be used to fertilize an entire clutch laid over a couple of days, or can be stored until the female is ready to lay at a later stage. For example, Grey Hornbills have been known to lay fertile eggs more than three weeks after being sealed off from their mates in the nest cavity.

INSIDE INFO

STREAMS OF BUBBLES

When boiling an egg you will notice streams of tiny bubbles rising from the shell. This is the air escaping from inside the egg through the tiny pores in the shell. A chicken's eggshell has as many as 10 000 pores. The blunt end of the egg usually floats, as this is where the air space is positioned in the egg. The chick breaks through into the air space just before hatching, and inhales its very first breath of air from within the shell.

EGG SHAPE AND SIZE

Although we use the term 'egg-shaped' to describe something roughly oval, in reality not all eggs conform to this traditional shape. Different bird species lay eggs that vary greatly in shape: some are almost round, while others lay eggs that are distinctly pointed at one end.

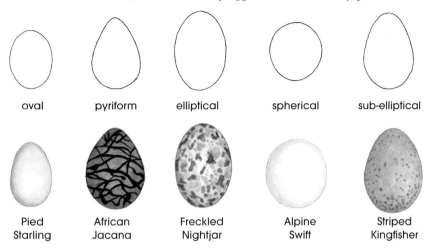

| oval | pyriform | elliptical | spherical | sub-elliptical |
| Pied Starling | African Jacana | Freckled Nightjar | Alpine Swift | Striped Kingfisher |

Bird eggs come in a wide range of different shapes.

The significance of shape

Shape plays an important role in an egg's survival, as it affects how the egg will roll if it is moved. Because birds turn their eggs fairly often while they are incubating (*see* page 97), or may bump the eggs inadvertently, it is important that they are shaped so that they don't roll out of the nest. While round eggs roll away relatively easily if pushed, eggs that are pointed at one end roll in circles and so stay within the nest area. For this reason, eggs that are laid in little more than a scrape on the open ground, such as those of plovers and coursers, are more pointed at one end than those of tree-nesting birds that have a secure nest to contain them. This pyriform shape is particularly important for cliff-nesting birds, as their eggs would smash on the rocks below if they rolled away from the nest area. Birds with the roundest eggs of all are generally hole-nesters; there is little danger that eggs contained deep within a tree or sandy tunnel will roll away.

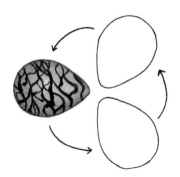

The pyriform egg of the African Jacana (LEFT) rolls in a tight circle if pushed, while the round egg of the hole-nesting Little Bee-eater (RIGHT) rolls in a fairly straight line.

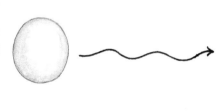

Egg shape is not necessarily always determined by how an egg will roll. For example, turacos lay their round eggs in flimsy, open, saucer-shaped nests in trees – not an ideal shape for such a precarious situation. It is possible that these eggs are shaped in the best way for the development of the embryo, rather than to prevent the egg from rolling away.

The Black-winged Stilt positions its eggs with the pointed ends facing inwards.

WEDGED IN

The eggs of ground-nesting birds, especially those that lay three to four eggs, such as jacanas, Black-winged Stilts and Pied Avocets, are often arranged neatly in the nest with their pointed ends all facing inwards. It is thought that this arrangement might help to 'wedge' the eggs in place to-gether in the nest, making them less likely to roll away, as well as keeping them in the best position for incubation.

Egg size

The relative size of a bird's egg can be determined by a number of factors. Generally, the bigger the bird, the larger the egg that it will lay – an obvious comparison being between the large, dinosaur-like eggs of the Common Ostrich and the tiny, pea-like eggs of sunbirds and finches.

The size of an egg also depends very much on whether the chicks hatch out naked and helpless (altricial), like those of most tree-nesters, or feathered and raring to go (precocial), like those of most ground-nesting birds (*see* Chapter 7, page 101). In birds with altricial chicks, the eggs are significantly smaller as the chicks hatch out at a much earlier stage of development. By comparison, a ground-nesting bird of about the same size will lay a much larger egg, with the chicks hatching out more fully developed, covered in feathers and able to walk.

Ground-nesting Blacksmith Lapwing egg vs tree-nesting Cape Turtle Dove egg

Ground-nesting White-fronted Plover egg vs tree-nesting Common Fiscal egg

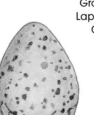

The egg size of ground nesters, whose chicks hatch well developed, is significantly bigger than that of similar sized tree nesters, whose chicks hatch poorly developed.

EGG COLOUR

The eggs of different bird species exhibit an astounding diversity in colour and markings, from dramatic streaks and blotches, fine spotting and shading, emphatic scribbles and scrawls, to classic, plain white or bright blue. One could imagine the calcium canvass of the eggshell reflecting a range of art periods: impressionism, cubism and expressionism are all represented in the avian art world.

While the colour and patterning of every egg laid is as individual and unique as a human's fingerprint, the general patterning is usually distinctive enough to show that it belongs to a particular species or group of birds.

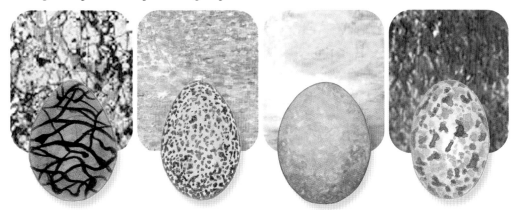

The patterns on eggshells may often resemble the styles of artists such as Pollock, Seurat, Turner and Van Gogh.

DIFFERENT PAINTING TECHNIQUES

The texture and pattern of paint on a canvas depends on the nature of the brushstrokes applied by the artist. Similarly, the distinctive patterning of blotches and streaks on the eggshell of a bird depend on whether the egg moves and spins as it passes the paintbrush-like pigment gland in the oviduct, or whether it is stationary and untwisting as the pigment is added.

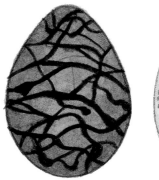
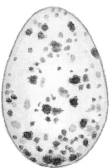

The dark streaks, smears and wavy lines around the African Jacana's egg show that it spins as it passes the point where the pigment gland secretes the colour. By contrast, the distinct, unsmeared spots on the egg of the Groundscraper Thrush show that it is stationary as the pigment is deposited.

Colouring the calcium canvas

Distinctive colours and unique patterns are deposited on the shell once the egg has formed and is moving down the female's oviduct just before being laid. Although the exact sequence and timing of this process varies from species to species, there are three main steps in colouring the eggshell of a bird:

❚ When the calcium carbonate shell is deposited around the egg during its development, it is usually whitish in colour. In some species it may be light blue.

❚ Later on in the egg's development a yellow pigment is added to the white shell, giving it a creamy or brownish colour. Light blue eggs become richer in colour, often with a greenish hue.

❚ Just before it is laid, the egg's distinctive blotches, streaks, spots or smears are added to the shell from a pigment gland in the oviduct. They are usually different shades of black, brown or red, and are derived from blood and bile.

In some species, the eggs are not altered beyond the first step, and are laid pure white or blue. Some are taken a step further, receiving a deeper overall colour, while other species take it a step further still and produce eggs with distinctive 'artistic' patterning.

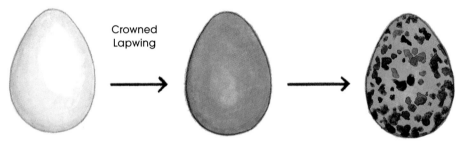

Crowned Lapwing

There are three main stages in the deposition of pigment: STEP 1: Calcium carbonate shell is initially white or light blue. STEP 2: Yellow pigment deepens the colour of the shell. STEP 3: The distinctive patterning is added from the pigment gland.

Bokmakierie

The role of egg colour

Attractive as eggs are, the real function of egg colour and patterning is not for aesthetics, but for camouflage, protecting them from the sharp eyes of hungry predators. The need for camouflage is largely determined by where the nest is built (if one is built at all), by the design of the nest, and by whether or not the parents are able to protect their eggs.

The amount of **camouflage colour** on the eggshell is usually directly related to just how vulnerable the egg is to predators, and the degree of 'invisiblility' that it needs to remain undetected.

Because most **ground-nesting birds** do not build a nest at all, but lay their eggs on the open ground, their clutch is most vulnerable to predation. Their eggs therefore need to be exceptionally well hidden, and so are usually decorated with more elaborate camouflage effects than any other eggs.

Nesting in a tree is safer and more protected than nesting on the open ground, so the eggs of **tree-nesting birds** have less colour camouflage than those of ground nesters.

Many birds lay **pure white eggs** with no camouflaging or patterning on the shell at all, making them highly visible to predators. In these species, eggs may not need to be camouflaged for a number of reasons.

The vulnerable eggs of the ground-nesting Crowned Lapwing have highly camouflaged markings.

The more secure location of tree nests, such as that of this Square-tailed Drongo, means the eggs require less camouflage than those of ground nesters.

MYSTERY COLOURS

It is difficult to find a good evolutionary reason for the bright blue or green eggs of certain birds, such as some chats, robin-chats, babblers and thrushes. It is thought that in these cases, egg colour may not be for camouflage, but may have another function, possibly a warning sign to predators that the eggs are inedible, or to reduce the chances of brood parasitism.

It is not fully understood why the eggs of the Arrow-marked Babbler are bright blue.

Hole and tunnel-nesting birds lay their eggs **out of sight** in a hole in a tree or a tunnel in a sandy bank, so they do not need to be camouflaged. Also, white eggs are thought to be more visible in the dark of a hole or burrow, and so are less likely to be inadvertently trampled by the parents.

Many large birds, such as raptors, defend their nests from predators, so their **eggs don't require camouflage** for protection. Even if the white eggs are seen by a predator, trying to steal them would be far too risky. In smaller species that lay white eggs, such as doves and nightjars, both parents share incubation duties, so the otherwise highly visible white eggs are always covered, seldom being left exposed to the keen eyes of predators.

In raptors, such as this Augur Buzzard, camouflage is unnecessary as the parents defend their eggs vigorously against predators.

The Little Bittern relies on the protection of the relatively inaccessible reedbed in which it breeds to protect its clutch rather than camouflage, hence the white eggs.

Many birds that **nest in safe areas** away from predators, for example on offshore islands or in reedbeds surrounded by a protective moat of water, don't need camouflaged eggs, as few predators are able to reach them.

Many large, colonially nesting birds, such as ibises, egrets, herons, cormorants and African Darters, find **safety in numbers**. They usually nest in areas protected from predators, and the combined eyes of the colony members provide an early-warning system should a predator be seen in the area. An additional advantage of colonial breeding is that individual eggs are less likely to be preyed upon if there are many others around from which a predator can choose.

Colonial nesting birds such as these Cattle Egrets find safety in numbers.

EGGS THAT 'CHANGE COLOUR'

In some species, eggs gradually change colour as incubation proceeds. For example, the eggs of the Bearded Vulture are white with light, shadow-like markings when first laid. As the parent birds incubate the eggs, the iron oxide pigment from their breast feathers rubs off on the eggs, soon staining them a rich, rusty brown colour. Grebes' eggs, too, are pure white when laid. Gradually the shell becomes brown and discoloured by the parent birds' wet feet and by the damp nesting material, which is used to cover the eggs when the parents leave the nest.

Iron oxide pigment from the incubating Bearded Vulture's breast feathers soon turns their pale eggs a rusty brown.

Different hues

While a certain degree of **variation in egg colour within a species** is the norm, some birds take this to the extreme. A number of birds, such as weavers and cisticolas, are known (across the species) to lay eggs of many different colours, so that it might almost appear as if they had been laid by totally different bird species. These are known as polychromatic eggs. However, an individual female does not lay eggs of many colours, but usually produces her own, typical egg colour throughout her life.

The eggs of the Southern Masked-Weaver show enormous colour variation, a possible defence strategy against being parasitized.

A reason could be that these birds are the ones most parasitized by brood parasites such as cuckoos and honeyguides. Having a variety of egg colours across the species makes it much more difficult for parasites to lay eggs that match those of the host, and the dumped eggs are therefore more likely to be noticed and rejected (*see* Chapter 8, page 116).

It was originally thought that colonial nesting birds found their nests in a vast breeding colony by being **able to recognize their own eggs**. However, this is now thought to be unlikely. Experiments have shown that it is more the nest site, and the mate on the nest with its individual call, to which the bird is drawn. Sometimes, however, birds do misjudge – although it is uncommon, gannets have been known to lay their single egg in the nest of a neighbour by mistake.

Although birds can't necessarily distinguish between the individual eggs in their clutch, some species are able to recognize if an egg is not their own. This is especially important for birds that are parasitized by other birds, as they can then eject the imposter eggs from the nest (*see* Chapter 8, page 116). On the other hand, many birds are totally undiscerning, and are known to sit happily on a brood of wooden or plastic eggs!

FAMILY PLANNING IN BIRDS

Each bird species has gradually evolved its own family planning strategy, the ultimate aim of which is for birds to produce as many healthy offspring as possible that will survive to adulthood, and ultimately produce young themselves. For some species, it's best to lay one egg per season, while other birds lay enormous clutches of up to 16 eggs, as well as extra clutches if conditions are favourable.

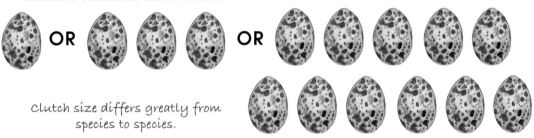

Clutch size differs greatly from species to species.

Scientists have often debated the reasons as to why different bird species have such different clutch sizes – a controversial question that has not yet been conclusively resolved. Some of the factors that are thought to play a role in determining clutch size are:

/ the number of eggs that a female is physically able to produce
/ the number of chicks that the parent(s) will be able to feed and defend
/ the largest number of eggs that a parent can cover and keep warm
/ whether birds are precocial (chicks active at birth) or altricial (chicks helpless at birth)
/ pressure from predators
/ seasonal and environmental factors such as food availability and weather
/ whether birds are long-lived (lay smaller clutches) or short-lived (lay larger clutches)
/ whether birds live in the tropics (lay smaller clutches) or in temperate areas
  (lay larger clutches).

The Double-banded Courser has evolved its own family planning strategy to cope with the trials of the harsh, arid environment in which it lives. Rather than laying one clutch of three to four eggs a season, it plays it safe and lays one egg three to four times a year. This means that, rather than losing a large clutch should pressures be too great, it risks losing just one chick and is able to start again without too much energy loss.

During times of low rainfall when food is scarce, the Spike-heeled Lark lays a small clutch of only two eggs. But when good rains fall they may lay as many as four to five eggs, and may also raise several broods to make up for fewer chicks reared during the dry months. The Helmeted Guineafowl 'puts all its eggs in one basket', laying a large clutch of up to 16 eggs.

The African Jacana's unusual family planning strategy is that of polyandry, in which the larger, more dominant female pairs with a number of different males, leaving them to incubate and rear the brood alone. This polyandrous habit has evolved to ensure that at least some of the offspring will survive the numerous threats of nesting in an aquatic habitat. These include the tendency of water bodies where the eggs are laid either to dry up or become flooded, leaving clutches non-viable, as well as the constant threat from a range of predators. Because the rate of nest failure is so high in these birds – in some cases over 80 per cent of clutches can be lost – a female would be wasting her energy if she invested all her time in incubation. Rather, her strategy of laying numerous clutches that are cared for by different males (sometimes in separate pans), spreads the risks and increases the chances that some of her offspring will survive.

The Helmeted Guineafowl (LEFT) 'puts all its eggs in one basket', laying up to 16 eggs, while the Double-banded Courser (ABOVE) lays a clutch of just one egg.

A nest-egg insurance policy

For some birds, laying an 'extra' egg is an unusual yet expedient strategy. For example, Wattled Cranes lay one or two eggs, but only ever raise one chick. Unlike most ground-nesting birds, which usually start incubating only after the whole clutch has been laid (*see* page 95), Wattled Cranes start incubating as soon as the first egg is laid. This gives the first egg a head start over the second, laid about two days later. Soon after the first chick hatches, the parents lead it away from the nest, abandoning the still egg-bound sibling a mere two days before it

Although up to two eggs are laid, the Wattled Crane only ever raises one chick.

hatches. A possible reason for this unusual behaviour is that Wattled Cranes are more likely to rear one chick successfully than two, as they can focus all their energies on feeding and protecting a single chick, rather than dividing their attention between two. The second egg is laid as an 'insurance policy' – should anything happen to the first egg, or should it turn out to be infertile, the cranes have a second chance. A similar situation is found in the Southern Ground-Hornbill.

Eggs ad infinitum

In some birds, the female's clutch is fixed at a certain number of eggs per breeding season, and she won't lay more even if eggs are removed or destroyed (**determinate laying**). In many species, however, the female is able to replace eggs that are lost. The female instinctively keeps laying, trying to reach her intuitive quota, which will signal her body to stop producing more eggs (**indeterminate laying**).

GETTING LAID
(some useful terms)

- **Single-brooded**: Where birds do not lay another clutch in a season after successfully raising one brood.
- **Double- or multiple-brooded**: Where two or more clutches are laid in one breeding season after a first brood is successfully reared. Many species produce extra broods if conditions are right.
- **Replacement clutch**: Where another clutch of eggs is laid to replace an earlier nest failure (as opposed to laying another clutch after breeding successfully).
- **Determinate laying**: Where a species' clutch size is set at a fixed number and a female won't lay any more eggs, even if eggs she has laid are removed or taken by predators.
- **Indeterminate laying**: Where a species is able to keep replacing eggs that are lost.

The ability of domestic hens to lay an egg every day, all year round, has been exploited by the egg-producing industry. Hens can be stimulated to start laying by placing an artificial egg in their nests, and farmers often place 'cheater' eggs made of wax, plastic or wood under hens to induce laying.

The case of 'yard' eggs

In some cases, birds such as flamingos and pelicans are known to lay and abandon single eggs in their 'loafing' areas. These are known as 'yard' eggs, and are often laid just before the breeding season. It could be that the birds' bodies are preparing for the breeding season, and that these eggs are produced early, prior to mating and nest building.

INCUBATION

Once an egg is laid and leaves the warmth and protection of the female's body, it needs to be incubated at the right temperature for the embryo to develop, usually between 35 and 38°C. The developing embryo is totally dependent on its parents to keep its egg 'sanctuary' warm, because at this stage it is not able to produce or control its own heat.

When to start incubating

Some birds start incubating after the first egg in the clutch is laid, while others wait until the entire clutch is complete. Given that eggs are laid at least one day apart, it could take several days for the whole clutch to be laid. When to start incubating depends largely on whether or not it is important for all the chicks to hatch out together.

The chicks of most ground-nesters, such as these Blue Cranes, hatch out at about the same time.

In most tree-nesters, such as wagtails, hatching is staggered.

In most ground-nesting birds it is important for all the chicks to hatch at about the same time (**synchronous hatching**), so that the whole clutch can be moved together away from the vulnerable nest site to a safer place. For this reason, the parents usually wait until all, or nearly all, of the eggs have been laid before starting to incubate. In this way, the embryos all develop at about the same rate and the feathered siblings will hatch out at roughly the same time. In some ground-nesters it is thought that the peeping of one chick as it begins to hatch may stimulate the other chicks into hatching mode. This is another way of ensuring that they will all hatch at about the same time.

In other bird species, mainly tree- and hole-nesters, **incubation starts as soon as the first egg is laid**, giving it a head start, in hatching and development, on eggs laid on subsequent days. Staggering the arrival of their chicks is thought, in part, to help avoid the huge, immediate demand on the parents to feed a nest full of hungry chicks all at once.

SPECIAL ANTENATAL CARE

Birds have evolved a range of ingenious techniques to ensure that their egg-bound embryos receive the best antenatal care.

The brood patch

During the breeding season, most incubating birds develop a special brood patch on their belly to keep the eggs at the optimal temperature for development. The feathers on an area of the belly are lost as a result of hormonal activity, leaving a patch of bare, warm skin that's perfect for incubating eggs. The brood patch is particularly warm because the blood vessels here dilate, allowing more blood to flow to the area, thereby heating the developing eggs. Depending on the clutch size, a bird may develop two or three brood patches. Generally, brood patches develop only in the sex that incubates.

It is rather odd that sometimes even cuckoos, which never incubate their own eggs or chicks, develop brood patches. The reason for this is unknown, but is likely a vestige from a time when they used to incubate their eggs themselves.

The position of the brood patches can be seen on the belly of this Pied Avocet.

ATTENTIVE FATHERS

Soon after the eggs are laid, male African Jacanas are abandoned by their mates and left to take full responsibility for incubating the eggs and raising the chicks alone. They are dedicated fathers, taking special care of their eggs. The incubating bird folds its wings under the eggs, holding them away from the damp, floating nest and against his warm brood patch. Jacanas usually lay a clutch of four eggs, so two are tucked up on each side of the body.

Although most birds have brood patches, a few species have evolved their own idiosyncratic incubation methods. Gannets have transferred their brood patch to their webbed feet, which act as warming pads when placed on the single egg. Ducks don't have a brood patch at all. They compensate by plucking their own breast feathers and using them to line the nest, providing a warm layer of insulation for their eggs.

Clever concealment

Some bird species, especially ground-nesters that lay their eggs in the open, have developed a habit of covering their eggs when they leave the nest unattended. It is thought that the eggs are covered to hide them from predators, as well as to maintain the temperature in the nest. They may be covered with nesting material, sand or by a layer of insulating feathers.

The Kittlitz's Plover always covers its eggs with nest-lining material when it leaves the nest unattended, kicking material in with its feet. The eggs of other species such as Crowned and Blacksmith lapwings are left half-buried in nest lining. Jacanas pull nesting material over their eggs and may leave the nest unattended for fairly long periods, while many ducks and geese cover their eggs with insulating down. Although camouflage was probably the primary reason why egg-covering evolved in these species, both the down in the case of waterfowl and the decaying plant material in that of jacanas may also help to retain and generate some heat in the nest.

Avian air-cooling system

Although it is well known that eggs have to be incubated to keep warm, some birds nesting in very hot, exposed places incubate

The African Black Duck covers its eggs with down feathers plucked from its own breast.

their eggs for the opposite reason – to keep them cool. The developing embryo is in fact much more sensitive to over-heating than it is to cooling, and many birds sit on their eggs to prevent the boiling hot conditions around them from over-heating and addling the eggs. Some birds, for example the Double-banded Courser, may also stand over their eggs, keeping them in their shadow while allowing any cooling wind that there might be to pass over them.

The Double-banded Courser straddles its single egg with wings drooped, shading it from the hot sun.

Egg wetting

The temperature on the ground in some areas can become very hot. For ground-nesting birds, this greatly increases the danger of their eggs overheating. To cool their eggs, some birds wet their belly feathers, a practice known as 'belly-soaking'. Belly-soaking is practised mainly by plovers, Black-winged Stilts, Pied Avocets and the African Skimmer.

Sunny side up

Incubating birds turn their eggs fairly regularly. It is thought that this helps to keep the embryos from sticking to the inside of the shell, and in large clutches, allows each egg a turn in the centre of the nest – the prime spot for incubation. It may also help to distribute heat more evenly in the egg, rather than on one side only. Egg turning also allows the embryo to settle into the best position for hatching.

Although the female Cape Batis incubates alone, the male may bring food to her at the nest.

Incubation duty

Depending on the species, parents take on different incubating duties. Either the female incubates alone, or both male and female share this parental duty by taking turns. In species such as robin-chats, thrushes, swallows, hornbills, cisticolas, sunbirds and starlings, the female incubates alone, while the male helps to feed the chicks once they hatch. Female raptors take

A Pied Avocet turns its eggs.

on almost full incubation duties, but the male provides support by bringing food to her at the nest, and helps to feed the chicks.

Examples of birds in which incubation and caring for the young are shared equally by both male and female include egrets, herons, storks, ibises, flamingos, cranes, kingfishers, waders, doves, pigeons and most seabirds. In the Common Ostrich, the shared incubation duties are scheduled for optimal concealment; the male incubates at night when his black-feathered body blends into the darkness of night, and the female incubates during the day, her drabber feathers camouflaged against the often dry, patchy landscape.

In very rare cases, such as in the African Jacana and the Greater Painted-Snipe, the male is left to incubate the eggs alone.

Do birds incubate constantly?

Depending on weather conditions, eggs do not necessarily need to be incubated all the time. On warm days, eggs can be left unattended for fairly long periods. Birds nesting

STUCK DOWN

Some birds don't turn their eggs, and some even can't. The African Palm-Swift, for example, uses its own saliva to glue its eggs to the simple nest it attaches precariously to a palm leaf, and so can't turn them. In this species, the eggs suffer no ill effects from not being turned.

African Palm-Swift eggs are stuck to the nest with sticky saliva.

in colder climates generally spend more time incubating than those in warmer climates. In species where incubation is shared by both the male and female, the parents take turns, and the eggs are incubated constantly. But where the female incubates alone, she has to take time off the nest to feed. As incubation proceeds, birds are able to leave the eggs unattended for longer periods of time, as the developing embryo is less sensitive to changes in temperature.

For how long are eggs incubated?

Once an egg is laid, how long does it take to hatch? The general rule is: the larger the egg, the longer the incubation period. Most of our large vultures have an incubation period of about 56 days, while the tiny Blue Waxbill, by comparison, has an incubation period of only 10 to 12 days.

Generally, ground-nesting birds that have precocial chicks have an incubation period almost double that of similar sized tree-nesting birds. This is because their chicks are well developed by the time they hatch – eyes open, feathered and able to walk – and so need more time to grow in the egg. The helpless chicks of tree-nesting species that enjoy a shorter incubation period hatch naked, closed-eyed and unable to walk. While the incubation period of the ground-nesting White-fronted Plover is about 27 days, that of the similar sized Common Fiscal is only 16–17 days. The Blacksmith Lapwing incubates for 29 days, while the incubation period of the similar sized Cape Turtle Dove is a mere 14 days.

BONE FOOD

Towards the end of the incubation period, the eggshell is much weaker than when it was first laid. This is because the chick has been absorbing calcium from the shell for its own bone development. Up to 80 per cent of a chick's calcium needs come from the shell.

BREAKING OUT: THE HATCHING PROCESS

Once the chick is ready to hatch, the shell that has been its life-sustaining sanctuary becomes a thin yet formidable barrier between the chick and its new life in the outside world. Breaking out of its calcium case is not an easy task for a chick. The process can take as little as a few hours in some species, or as long as a couple of days in others.

A day or two before the chick hatches, it breaks through the shell membranes into the air space at the blunt end of the shell, and starts breathing air into its lungs for the first time. It may now be heard peeping from inside the shell. Until then, it is supplied with oxygen that enters the egg through the porous shell and is carried to the chick via blood vessels.

To aid its escape from the shell, the chick has had to evolve 'Houdini-like' escape tactics. A special muscle developed at the back of its neck helps it push hard against the shell, while it uses a hard egg 'tooth' at the tip of the bill to chip its way slowly out. The chick takes many breaks in its exhausting efforts to break out. The shell eventually cracks open at the blunt end, and the weary chick enters its new world.

THE EGG 'TOOTH': A REPTILIAN RELIC

Like birds, reptiles such as snakes and lizards also have an egg 'tooth' that they use to escape from their shells, a sure sign of birds' reptilian ancestry. Both birds and reptiles lose the 'tooth' soon after hatching.

MUSCLING OUT

The chicks of the Common Ostrich do not have egg 'teeth' to help them break out. Instead, they use a series of strong muscular contractions to push against the shell and crack it open.

From a home to a hazard

Once the chick hatches, the egg that once sustained life becomes a potential danger to the brood – the white insides of the broken egg can easily be spotted by hungry predators. For this reason, the parents either remove the shells and drop them away from the nest or even, in the case of cranes, for instance, eat the empty shells, which are a good source of calcium.

7 CHICKS

ONCE A CHICK HAS LEFT THE EGG, THE CHALLENGES OF LIFE HAVE ONLY JUST BEGUN. While some chicks are born naked, helpless and totally dependent on their parents for their every need, others hatch out feathered, active and largely independent. For both types, there are numerous obstacles to be negotiated, and for this reason, only a small percentage of birds survive to reach adulthood.

Much of chicks' 'avian education' occurs during the sensitive imprinting stage, when they acquire life-skills essential for their survival. In addition to a sound education, good nutrition is vital to their development, and different species of birds offer menus specifically suited to the needs of their growing chicks. Some even get specially prepared *cordon bleu* meals such as the predigested and regurgitated seafood gruel of seabirds, the special protein-rich 'milk' of doves and pigeons, and the saliva-coated insects of swifts.

Whiskered Tern and chicks

NAKED AND HELPLESS OR FEATHERED AND MOBILE?

Newly hatched chicks of different species, although identical in age, may appear and behave completely differently. They fall into two main groups – altricial and precocial chicks.

Naked and helpless: altricial chicks

Some chicks hatch naked, blind and virtually immobile, and are therefore completely dependent on their parents for food and protection. These are known as altricial chicks. They have weak legs, and are unable to walk or move around until older. Their brains are small and at this young age, they are not able to control their own body temperature, relying on their parents for warmth. Most tree- and hole-nesting birds fall into this group.

Feathered and mobile: precocial chicks

Other chicks hatch well developed and are covered with a layer of fuzzy down feathers. They are born with their eyes open, are alert and mobile and able to move around independently in search of food almost immediately after hatching. These are known as precocial chicks. Their brains are quite large compared with those of altricial chicks and they are also able to regulate their own body temperature soon after they hatch. The eggs of precocial chicks are incubated for a longer period of time than those of altricial chicks, enabling them to hatch out at a more advanced stage of development. This group comprises mainly ground-nesting birds.

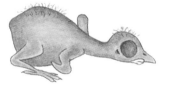

An altricial Lesser Masked-Weaver chick (LEFT) clearly differs from the precocial Crowned Lapwing chick (RIGHT) of the same age.

VARIATIONS ON THE THEME

Not all newly hatched chicks fall neatly into either the 'altricial' or 'precocial' categories, but may lie somewhere in between. For example, the chicks of raptors, herons and egrets are said to be 'semi-altricial' as they hatch with their eyes open and covered in a layer of down, but are immobile and nest-bound and totally dependent on their parents for food. The chicks of species such as oystercatchers, terns and grebes are 'semi-precocial' as they are active and mobile at birth and leave the nest soon after hatching, but still rely on their parents for food.

A semi-altricial Black Sparrowhawk chick

How safe is the home?

The location of the nest largely determines whether the chicks can remain helpless for a long period or whether they need to be active at birth. The nests of tree- and hole-nesting altricial birds are generally built in a relatively more secure position than those of ground-nesting species. Chicks are much safer in the shelter of the nest, and can develop more slowly, and therefore hatch at a much earlier stage in their development. By comparison, parents of precocial chicks experience the 'empty nest syndrome' much sooner. The nests of these ground-nesting species, such as plovers, lapwings, cranes, guineafowl and francolin, do not give chicks much protection from predators, and chicks must therefore be able to leave the nest and move away to safer hiding places from as young an age as possible.

Diet is also thought to play a role, as most (but not all) precocial chickds feed themselves soon after hatching, which they are able to do at ground level before they can fly.

Altricial species such as Arrow-marked Babblers nest in secure locations.

Precocial species such as Blue Cranes typically nest on the ground.

CHILDHOOD CHALLENGES

With potential dangers lurking behind every bush and grass clump and from the open sky, adult birds are constantly on the lookout for predators in order to warn their chicks of approaching danger with a series of alarm calls. Chicks need to learn a number of vital survival skills rapidly upon hatching if they are to have even a remote chance of surviving.

Predation

Because young chicks can't make an aerial getaway, they are much more vulnerable to predation than adults, and numerous predators make the most of the chicks' defenseless earth-bound state while they can. Mammal predators include mongooses, genets, baboons, monkeys and otters, while agile reptile

Baboons are opportunistic hunters and will not pass up the chance of preying on vulnerable Egyptian Goose chicks despite the brave resistance of the parents.

predators come in the form of monitor lizards and snakes. Chicks also come under avian attack from birds such as Pearl-spotted Owlets, Lizard Buzzards and goshawks. The African Harrier-Hawk has developed such a taste for young birds that it has evolved unusually long and double-jointed legs, enabling it to reach far into the holes of tree-nesting species in order to drag out the struggling chicks.

Overheating

Overheating of eggs and chicks is a real problem for many birds nesting in exposed sites, such as high up in trees with little cover, or exposed on the open ground. While many birds can regulate the temperature of their eggs through incubation, it is more difficult to protect chicks from the harsh sun once they hatch. In order to provide shade, certain adults raptors 'mantle' over the chicks with their wings spread out. In some cases stork chicks, sitting exposed on their stick platforms out in the open, are in serious danger of becoming overheated, and so occasionally the parents bring stomach-fulls of water to the nest, which they regurgitate over their young as a cooling shower. Some herons cool their chicks in a less hygienic way by defecating over their babies in a relieving but undignified shower.

An African Harrier-Hawk mantles over its chick, shading it from the hot sun.

Sibling rivalry

Sibling rivalry is not limited to humans, and can be taken to drastic extremes in the bird world, where young chicks often compete aggressively for parental care. In species where one egg hatches before the other, the chick that hatches first is often significantly bigger than its sibling. The larger chick generally overpowers its weaker sibling to ensure that it always gets the first pickings of food delivered by the parents. In some cases, this competition can even result in one chick killing its sibling.

In most cases, the chicks are not persecuted aggressively, but die of starvation or are trampled to death by their siblings in the stiff competition for food. Examples include hornbills, herons and boobies. In a few species, chicks are born with an aggressive, instinctive urge to attack and kill their younger sibling. This phenomenon is appropriately called siblicide, or 'cainism', after the biblical story of Cain, who killed his younger brother Abel in a fit of jealous rivalry. This seemingly ruthless act is in fact a fairly common method of brood reduction in the nests of some eagles and pelicans. In certain eagles, two eggs are laid, but invariably only one of the chicks survives to adulthood. In a study on the Verreauxs' Eagle, it was found that in only one in 200 cases did both chicks survive to fledgling. In very rare cases the winner has been known to eat the loser in order not to waste the nutrients invested by the parents in the extra egg.

A Verreauxs' Eagle chick kills its younger sibling, a form of behaviour known as 'siblicide'.

Although the precise reason for this behaviour is still unclear, it is thought to be a form of insurance by the adults – if one egg does not hatch or if one chick dies, there is another to take its place. It might also be too costly for the parents to raise both young – it is better to raise one healthy chick than two weaker ones with lower chances of survival.

Survival skills

In order to survive the constant threat of hidden dangers, both parents and chicks have developed a range of survival skills to give them a fair chance of outsmarting their enemies.

Well-camouflaged Crowned Lapwing chicks crouch down when the alarm is given.

CHICKS ON RED ALERT

In response to a parent's alarm call, the chicks' survival instinct kicks in and they react immediately by crouching and remaining still until the predator has passed, or they dash for cover. The adult calls again to indicate when the coast is clear. In species such as plovers and thick-knees, another type of alarm call results in all the chicks rushing to safety beneath the parents' wings for warmth or protection.

INTREPID PARENTS

In addition to sounding the alarm to warn their chicks of danger, parents are sometimes prepared to risk their own lives to protect their offspring. A number of ground-nesting birds such as waders, lapwings and larks feign injury in order to distract potential predators and lead them away from their eggs or chicks. The best known of these is the 'broken wing display', where the parent feigns injury and leads the predator away from its chicks with its wing hanging, then flies off at the last moment when the predator attempts to capture it.

Some species take a more aggressive approach to predators. Thick-knees, lapwings and owls often spread their wings in a dramatic threat display and may even dive-bomb an intruder while calling incessantly, either veering away at the last minute or sometimes actually making contact and inflicting injuries with their claws or bills. Other bird species may gang together to mob predators such as owls or snakes to protect their chicks (*see* Chapter 9, page 127). The hole-nesting Southern Black Tit is another intrepid parent with an extraordinary tactic for deterring predators: the female sits tight on her nest if approached, producing a loud snake-like hissing sound to fool intruders into thinking that a dangerous snake is lurking within.

The Spotted Thick-knee defends its chicks by spreading its wings
in an intimidating threat display.

A Spike-heeled Lark removes a faecal sac from its nest to keep it clean.

SNEAKING BACK HOME

Parent birds usually approach their nest surreptitiously so that they do not reveal its position to potential predators. They may sit and wait for a considerable time until it is certain that the coast is clear and their arrival is not being watched.

HOUSEHOLD HYGIENE

Most birds are fastidious about keeping their nests as clean as possible, as this limits tell-tale signs of nesting activity that would otherwise be detected by predators, as well as keeping down the risk of disease and infection.

Many parent birds habitually remove their chicks' faeces from the nest. The faeces is often enclosed in a white gelatinous sac. This is carried away and discarded at a safe distance. The chicks of some hole-nesting birds, such as hornbills, back up to the nest entrance, lift their tails and squirt their faeces as far away from the nest as possible. Other species, such as turacos and mousebirds, are known to swallow their chicks' droppings which, because of the chicks' poorly developed digestive tracts, still contain useful nutrients.

FOULED FEATHERS

Not all species value hygiene, and fouling of the nest is not uncommon. Many tunnel nesters are known to have highly unsanitary nests, so much so that some kingfishers need to dip into water frequently in order to clean their feathers after leaving their fouled nests. African Hoopoe chicks have evolved a special strategy to remain clean in their soiled nests. Unlike those of most birds, their new feathers remain in their protective sheaths until just before they leave the nest to prevent them from becoming fouled. The nests of many raptors, pigeons and finches are also known for their filthy conditions, as these birds seldom remove the faeces of their young.

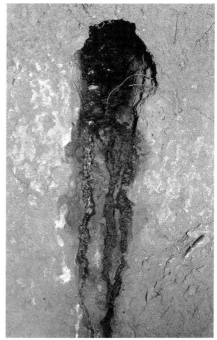

Liquid faeces oozes from the fouled nest of a Malachite Kingfisher.

JACANAS IN JEOPARDY

Jacana chicks use two ingenious strategies to ensure their personal safety. One is to dive underwater and leave only their bill showing above the surface like a snorkel – a survival tactic not used by the adults. The second is to be lifted to safety and carried away under the male's protective wings, the only indication of the chicks' presence being their distinctively long, spindly toes dangling almost comically below the adult's undercarriage. Grebe parents also carry their chicks to safety, placing them on their backs instead of under their wings.

Only the toes of the African Jacana's chicks are visible, dangling from beneath their father's wings.

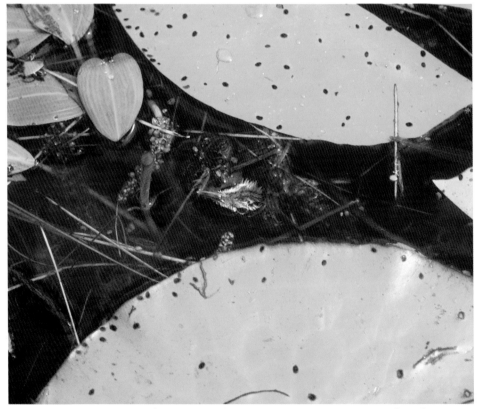

A Lesser Jacana chick seeks refuge beneath the water. Only its bill, which it uses like a snorkel to breathe, is visible.

Young Water Thick-knees imprint on their parents within the first few days of hatching.

IMPRINTING: ESSENTIAL AVIAN EDUCATION

A young chick's avian education is a rigorous and intensive process during which it learns life skills that are essential for their survival in a demanding and hostile world. The most important learning period occurs during a stage known as imprinting.

The first image a chick sees when it hatches is that of its parents, and it imprints on them almost immediately. This allows the chick to recognize, bond with and respond to its parents. Imprinting on their parents usually happens within the first two days of hatching in precocial chicks, because they leave the nest soon after hatching and need to follow the mother closely.

Chicks in a bustling Sacred Ibis colony wait patiently to be fed.

This occurs a lot earlier than in altricial chicks which can safely stay in the nest for much longer periods. So strong is this instinct that a chick may imprint on any substitute it sees in place of its parents as it hatches. There have been cases of chicks imprinting on people, clocks, toys, shadows and even cars.

Growing chicks do not only imprint on their parents, however. Song development, recognizing birds of their own species and avoiding predators are other abilities that become imprinted during additional 'sensitive' growing periods. They also imprint on appropriate nest materials and nest sites, which will be important when they come to rear their own young. The sensitive period for sexual imprinting happens at a later stage of development, usually when chicks are growing their adult plumage.

It is only during these sensitive periods that learned behaviour becomes fixed and will never be forgotten. Outside of these periods additional learning either doesn't occur or is much less effective.

A CHICK'S NUTRITIOUS MENU

Parent birds work continuously and seemingly inexhaustibly to provide their chicks with the most nutritious food available. Depending on the species, chicks are offered varied menus, from fresh meat severed into bite-sized pieces (in the case of most raptors), to a nutritious regurgitated seed mix (for seed-eaters), protein-rich invertebrates (for insectivores), or a predigested seafood gruel in the case of some seabirds.

The regularity with which adults deliver food to their young varies greatly from species to species. Among small birds with large broods, parents follow a hectic schedule, delivering food as often as once every minute, although four to 12 times an hour is the average for passerines. Trogons bring food to the nest once every hour, and Barn Owls, on average, 10 times a night. Among large raptors, parents may deliver food only once or twice daily, while some albatross chicks may wait patiently for up to three days between meals as their parents travel vast distances in search of food.

An adult African Hoopoe brings back an insect to its hungry chicks.

An African Spoonbill regurgitates a nutritious fishy gruel into a hungry chick's mouth.

Predigested meals

Many seabirds regurgitate a half-digested fishy gruel directly into the chick's begging mouth. They carry this food back to their chicks in their crop and stomach, which act as storage pouches, enabling them to carry more food per trip. This is important, given the vast distances that they often need to travel in search of food. Another important advantage of food regurgitated from the crop and stomach is that it contains some of the adults' digestive juices, a necessary boost for the young chicks' poorly developed digestive system. Many seabirds actually need to delay digestion, however, because their commute is so long that they might otherwise arrive back at the nest with the food already digested.

Balls of saliva

Because swifts feed on tiny insect prey – appropriately called 'plankton of the air' – it is not worth their while to return to the nest each time they catch a minute insect. Rather, they accumulate a ball of food mixed with

A White-rumped Swift arrives at its nest with a bulging throat containing a saliva ball full of insects.

saliva in their gular, or throat pouch. A single saliva ball may contain an astounding 1 200 items. When the chicks are small, the saliva ball is first broken into manageable pieces before being fed to them, but when they are older, it is presented whole.

Pigeon milk

Doves and pigeons produce a nutritious liquid from their crop, known as 'pigeon milk' which they use to feed their chicks.

ACTIVE INSECTS

Most insectivorous birds feed their young by placing insects straight into their gaping mouths. The insect is usually pushed fairly far down their throats to induce the swallowing reflex – if the chicks don't swallow quickly enough, live insects might just crawl right out of their mouths.

This special liquid is produced by both sexes and is made up of nutritious fluids full of small food fragments and fat-laden cells sloughed off from the lining of the crop. Like the milk of mammals, this fluid is rich in protein and fats, including essential amino acids. It is also thought to contain important antibodies, which help build up the chicks' immune system. A similar nutritious milk is produced by flamingos and Emperor Penguins. In all birds that produce this milk, the clutch size is small (either one or two chicks), as it would be difficult for the parents to produce sufficient milk to support more chicks.

A Namaqua Dove feeds both chicks simultaneously on pigeon milk 'formula'.

Protein supplements

Although the diet of adult seed-eaters and fruit-eaters is predominantly vegetarian, they need to feed their growing chicks a 'protein supplement' in the form of insects, especially during the very early stages of their development. This is because fruits and seeds alone do not contain sufficient protein (or water) for nestling growth and so need to be complemented by protein-rich insects.

EARLY LEARNING INSIDE THE EGG

The chicks of the Crowned Lapwing imprint on the sounds and smells outside the egg even before they hatch.

It has been found that chicks are able to learn about sounds and odours even before they hatch, much as human babies are able to hear sounds from inside the womb. From their sanctuary within the egg, chicks can hear the songs and calls of the adults and are thought to begin imprinting on their vocalizations even at this very early stage. They are also able to detect odours of the nest and their parents through the porous eggshell. Therefore, when a chick hatches, it is already somewhat familiar with certain aspects of its new world.

THE 'EMPTY-NEST' SYNDROME

Soon, the chick has to get ready for the pivotal event in its life – leaving the nest. As the chick grows, feathers start appearing from small pockets in the skin. These new feathers are initially encased in a sheath or pin, but soon burst free. Once the feather has fully emerged, the core of blood vessels is absorbed back into the skin, and the hollow central quill and the vane on either side harden.

Long before they are ready to leave the nest or fly, young birds 'work out' to build up their strength. For example, young pelicans and raptors spend hours every day stretching, beating their wings and also bouncing up and down on their nests, strengthening their wing muscles and generally getting a feel for what it would be like to be airborne.

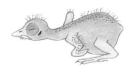

Day 1: Totally naked with eyes closed.

Day 4: Feather pins begin to show on wings.

Day 6: More pins begin to show on wings and body. Eyes begin to open.

Day 10: Feathers begin to break through the tips of the pins.

Day 12: More feathers break through the pins. The chick is now able to support itself.

Day 16: Young bird still has a fleshy gape, short tail and light iris. It will soon moult into full adult plumage.

Stages of development of an altricial Lesser Masked-Weaver chick

GROWTH RATES

The growth rates of chicks of different species can vary hugely, from the rapid 11–13 day fledging period of the Red-billed Quelea, to that of the Wandering Albatross, which has the longest known nesting period of up to 303 days. The nestlings of altricial species often grow three to four times faster than the chicks of precocial birds. To ensure that they survive during periods of limited food supply, some chicks build up fat reserves to tide them over. It is also used as a back-up food supply for the days just after fledging, when the chick is learning to feed itself. (The chicks of precocial birds are not called nestlings as they do not remain in the nest.)

ATTENTION GRABBING

Altricial chicks beg persistently for food, craning their necks upwards and opening their beaks at the slightest vibration that might suggest that one of their parents has arrived with food. The chicks' brightly coloured mouths and gapes are extremely sensitive and the lightest touch or movement of the nest will cause the chick to open its beak and beg. The colourful gapes are a garish signal telling the parents where the food should be placed, as well as indicating which chicks among the brood have just been fed and which are still hungry.

These hungry African Paradise-Flycatcher chicks are begging persistently.

Young African Palm-Swift chicks cling to palm fronds before their first flight.

This Cape White-eye chick has just left the safety of the nest.

As fledglings leave the sanctuary of the nest, they become more vulnerable to predators, as well as to harsh weather conditions. Once they have survived the first few dangerous days, however, the chicks may be safer than they were back in the nest, and their survival rate begins to improve.

Fledglings of most small passerines stay with their parents for several weeks after leaving the safety of the nest, learning a range of survival skills, such as how to forage, avoid predators and interact with members of their own species.

A Tawny Eagle chick enjoys a perfect 'bird's-eye view' from the safety of its nest.

AVIAN KINDERGARTENS

Many colonial species, such as penguins, flamingos and pelicans, leave their chicks in special 'crèches', while the parents are away feeding. Although birds may gather together in large groups, parents and chicks have the remarkable ability of being able to recognize each other on the parents' return, largely by identifying individual calls.

White Pelicans leave their chicks in the safety of avian 'crèches'.

8 FOSTER FAMILIES

Photo by Hugh Chittenden

PLACING OFFSPRING IN FOSTER CARE IS NOT LIMITED TO HUMAN SOCIETY. Certain bird species also put their chicks up for adoption – only without the consent or even knowledge of the hood-winked adoptive parents. This phenomenon is known as 'brood parasitism'.

Once the female parasite locates the nest of a potential host, she waits patiently nearby until the host leaves its nest during a pause in egg-laying or incubation. The parasite then slips into the nest, hastily lays an egg and flies off, never to see its offspring again. When the host returns, it usually cannot distinguish the parasite's egg from its own and automatically accepts the addition to its clutch, incubates the egg and hatches and raises the chick.

As the ungrateful chick grows up into a demanding foster fledgling, the host becomes an involuntary and defenceless slave, responding to all the parasite's needs, toiling away, oblivious to the fact that this monster chick can in no way be its own, and this despite the fact that the young parasite can be up to three or four times larger than the parent. The fledgling eventually leaves the nest, still being fed by the exhausted foster parents and, once it becomes an adult, begins the own search for its victim.

OPPOSITE: A rare image of an Olive Sunbird feeding a Klaas's Cuckoo chick on pigeonwood (Trema orientalis) berries. This is highly unusual, as cuckoos are usually strictly insectivorous and are not known to eat berries.

The Diderick Cuckoo is a notorious parasite, with as many as 24 different host species.

BROOD PARASITES

Although cuckoos are the best known brood parasites, there are a number of other brood parasites occurring in southern Africa, each having evolved its own ingenious method of fooling its host. These include the honeyguides and honeybirds, the whydahs and indigobirds, as well as the enigmatic Cuckoo Finch. Each of these groups of parasite families displays certain diagnostic traits.

Cuckoos

Ten cuckoo species breed in southern Africa. While most cuckoos parasitize a number of different host species, a few have only one host. Host species include robin-chats, shrikes, starlings, babblers, bulbuls, warblers, sunbirds, weavers and wagtails. A single egg is usually laid per nest. Egg colour and pattern usually, but not always, match those of

the host. Incubation periods are usually shorter than those of the host, giving the parasite chick an advantage over host chicks as it hatches out earlier. The host usually raises the parasite chick alone, as its own eggs or chicks have been destroyed, either by the female brood parasite or its chick.

Honeyguides and honeybirds

Four honeyguide and two honeybird species occur in southern Africa. All species, except the Green-backed Honeybird (which is only known to parasitize the African Yellow White-eye), have more than one host. Host species include hole-nesting birds such as barbets, woodpeckers and kingfishers, as well as cisticolas, warblers and white-eyes. A single egg is usually laid per nest. Eggs do not need to match those of the host, as honeyguides and honeybirds usually parasitize hole-nesting birds or those with closed nests, where differences would not be clearly visible in the dark. Newly hatched chicks have sharp, lethal bill hooks that they use to kill the host chicks. Chicks remain in the nest for a long time, and are almost independent on leaving.

A Lesser Honeyguide chick emerges from the nest of its Black-collared Barbet host.

Whydahs and indigobirds

Eight species occur in southern Africa – four whydahs and four indigobirds. While most species are host-specific, some have more than one host. Whydahs parasitize specific waxbill and manikin species, while indigobirds parasitize specific firefinches. Eggs match those of the hosts. Only one egg is usually laid, but occasionally different females may parasitize the same nest – up to five different eggs have been recorded. In some species, as many as 26 eggs may be laid by one bird in a season. Birds do not remove or damage host eggs when laying their own eggs in the nest, and parasite and host chicks may be raised together, although the host chicks' chances of survival are reduced. The begging call, as well as the distinctive colour and patterns on the parasite chicks' mouth parts, mimic those of host chicks. This promotes acceptance of imposter chicks.

Cuckoo Finch

Originally thought to be a member of the weaver family (also known as the Parasitic Weaver), the Cuckoo Finch is now known to be more closely related to whydahs and indigobirds. It has at least 13 known host species (mainly cisticolas and prinias). Eggs match those of the host. It removes the host's eggs from the nest, and lays one to two eggs per nest.

TACTICS FOR TAKEOVER

 In order to ensure that their chicks receive the best foster care possible, brood parasites have evolved a remarkable array of tactics to deceive, outwit and take advantage of their unsuspecting hosts. Among their ploys are:

▌ Many parasites have evolved **eggs that closely mimic those of their hosts,** making it impossible for the host to tell them apart from their own eggs.

▌ Many brood parasites have **shorter incubation periods** than their hosts and thus their chicks hatch earlier, giving them a survival advantage. In cuckoos, this is because the embryo actually starts developing while the egg is still inside the female, unlike most other species, where development only starts once the egg is laid and is being incubated.

▌ Many cuckoos are able to **lay eggs in a matter of a few seconds**, while most bird species take a few minutes. This allows the parasite to lay quickly before the absent host returns.

▌ Cuckoo eggs are often **thicker shelled** and more **resistant to cracking** than other eggs, so they have less chance of breaking when laid in haste.

▌ Some adult cuckoos are known to **eject the host's eggs from the nest** and even trample its chicks to death.

▌ Some brood parasite chicks are aggressive from the start, and it is not uncommon for a hatchling cuckoo instinctively to **push the host's unhatched eggs or chicks out of the**

Note the distinctive concave back of this Emerald Cuckoo chick, with which it has just evicted the eggs of its host.

A female Klaas's Cuckoo 'caught in the act' leaves the nest of the Olive Sunbird it has just parasitized.

nest. Although blind and helpless looking, the young parasitic cuckoo is equipped with a concave back, very strong feet and stiff, outstretched wing stubs, which enable it to accomplish this seemingly vindictive task. This eviction impulse is

known to last up to five days. Whydah and indigobird chicks do not have this instinctive tendency, and are raised with the host chicks.

▮ After hatching, the brood parasite chick may **develop more rapidly** than the host's (generally smaller) offspring. Because of its large size, it competes aggressively for parental feeding, rendering the true host's offspring progressively weaker as the parasite chick develops. The host's own chicks often die as a result.

▮ Many chicks, such as those of indigobirds and whydahs, have **mouth and gape markings that mimic almost exactly those of the host's offspring**. This ensures that they will be accepted and fed, as the adults would not feed nestlings with the wrong markings.

▮ Besides egg mimicry, many brood parasites also show **plumage mimicry**. Feathered young Red-chested Cuckoos may initially appear similar to their Cape Robin-Chat hosts – before they rapidly outgrow their host siblings.

▮ Honeyguide and honeybird chicks have evolved sharp, fang-like **bill hooks on the tip of each mandible**. Upon hatching, they instinctively use the hooks to bite the host's offspring to death. These hooks are lost within a few days of hatching. Only one parasite egg is laid per nest, otherwise chicks would kill one another.

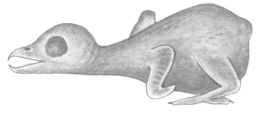

Honeyguides have evolved sharp, fang-like bill hooks on the tip of each mandible to kill their hosts' chicks.

ONE HOST OR MANY?

Most brood parasites are 'generalists', which means they parasitize a number of different host species. The Red-chested Cuckoo is an example of a generalist, and parasitizes various species of robin-chats, chats, thrushes and flycatchers. Honeyguides and honeybirds parasitize an array of mainly hole-nesting birds such as kingfishers, barbets, woodpeckers, wood-hoopoes and starlings. The record for the largest number of host species goes to the Greater Honeyguide, which parasitizes a least 29 different species.

By contrast, a number of 'host-specific' brood parasites apparently only ever parasitize one host species. The Thick-billed Cuckoo only ever lays its eggs in the nest of the Retz's Helmet-Shrike, while the Violet-eared Waxbill is sole host of the Shaft-tailed Whydah. Firefinches and twinspots are thought to be exclusive hosts of most indigobird parasites.

EGGS: TO MATCH OR NOT TO MATCH?

Many brood parasites have evolved eggs that closely resemble those of their hosts, so much so that the hosts do not recognize them as imposter eggs but accept them as their own. Parasites that portray this characteristic are known as 'matchers', while those that lay eggs of a different colour and size to their hosts are known as 'non-matchers'.

Similarly, host species are either 'discriminators' or 'non-discriminators'. Discriminators can tell the difference between their own eggs and those of other birds, and will reject any foreign eggs. By contrast, non-discriminators cannot tell the difference, and unwittingly incubate foreign eggs.

This Dark-capped Bulbul nest, parasitized by a Jacobin Cuckoo, is an example of a non-discriminator being parasitized by a non-matcher.

This Retz's Helmet-Shrike nest, parasitized by a Thick-billed Cuckoo, is an example of a discriminator being parasitized by a matcher.

For example, the speckled eggs of the Thick-billed Cuckoo (a matcher) closely resemble those of the Retz's Helmet-Shrike in both size and colour. The Retz's Helmet-Shrike would notice if the eggs of the Thick-billed Cuckoo differed from its own and would evict them; it is therefore a discriminator. On the other hand, the plain eggs of the Jacobin Cuckoo (a non-matcher) are markedly different from the speckled eggs of its Dark-capped Bulbul host. The Dark-capped Bulbul cannot tell the difference and is there-fore a non-discriminator.

EVOLUTION OF BROOD PARASITISM

Nobody knows exactly how brood parasitism evolved, but it's an intriguing issue and has been the subject of much study. It's clear that it evolved independently in the three parasitizing families – cuckoos, honeyguides and honeybirds, and viduids (whydahs and indigobirds) – and therefore one can assume that it's a strategy of considerable advan-tage to these birds. On the other hand, only a very small

An Orange-breasted Waxbill uses an old Southern Red Bishop nest. This behaviour is thought to have been the first step in the evolution of brood parasitism.

number of bird species are parasitic (only about one per cent of all birds worldwide) and no parasitic species is exceptionally common, which makes one question whether this strategy really is so beneficial.

Although it is still open to debate, ornithologists have proposed four possible steps that might have led to the evolution of brood parasitism in birds:

1 Many birds use the old, abandoned nests of other species for breeding, but still incubate their own eggs and rear their own young. Some examples include the Mocking Cliff-Chat, which takes over old swallow nests, the Bronze Mannikin, which sometimes uses old weaver nests, and the Orange-breasted Waxbill, which is known to use old nests of the Southern Red Bishop.

2 The next step might be the active take-over of occupied nests belonging to other bird species, particularly at the time of nest building and egg laying, and the eviction of the rightful occupants.

3 A bird that normally rears its own young may lay an egg in the nest of another bird of its own species, leaving that bird to raise its chick. This is, in fact, quite widespread, and occurs in many grebes, gulls and passerines such as the Common Starling. It occurs more often when there is a shortage of nest sites and when population density is high.

4 The final step would be when a species *must* lay its eggs in the nest of another species because it has lost the tendency and ability to incubate its own eggs, resulting in true brood parasitism. The cuckoos, honeyguides, honeybirds, whydahs, indigobirds and Cuckoo Finch fall into this category.

INSIDE INFO

THE ADVANTAGES OF BEING A PARASITE

Not having to invest large amounts of time and energy in nest building and incubating and rearing their own young enables brood parasites to channel their energy and resources into laying more eggs. Some species have been known to lay an incredible 26 eggs in one season. Avoiding 'putting all their eggs into one basket' and rather laying in a number of different nests improves the chances that some of the brood parasite's offspring will survive. This 'free ride' gives brood parasites more time to feed, establish their territory and increase their fitness, which means they can lay more eggs and have more broods raised.

A Village Weaver feeds a Diderick Cuckoo chick.

THE DEVIOUS BUT INGENIOUS DIDERICK

The Diderick Cuckoo and its ongoing parasitic relationship with its hosts is a good example of the 'evolutionary arms race' in progress. The Diderick Cuckoo has at least 24 host species; the record number for southern African cuckoos.

Through natural selection, different populations of the cuckoo, called 'gentes', have evolved, each matching the eggs of a specific host group. For example, one gente will parasitize only the Southern Masked-Weaver, while another will parasitize only the Southern Red Bishop. The gente gene is passed on by the female; so while she may mate with any male cuckoo, her specific gente lineage and egg-matching ability will be passed on to her female offspring, who will lay eggs in the nests of the species that reared them. It is thought that each gente recognizes the song and appearance of its specific host as a result of being raised by them.

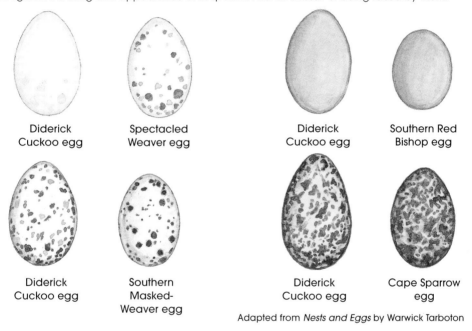

| Diderick Cuckoo egg | Spectacled Weaver egg | | Diderick Cuckoo egg | Southern Red Bishop egg |

| Diderick Cuckoo egg | Southern Masked-Weaver egg | | Diderick Cuckoo egg | Cape Sparrow egg |

Adapted from *Nests and Eggs* by Warwick Tarboton

EVOLUTIONARY ARMS RACE: A BATTLE BETWEEN PARASITE AND HOST

While many hosts have no defence against the strategy of brood parasitism, some species have evolved counter-tactics as a means of keeping ahead in what might be termed an 'evolutionary arms race'.

The egg-matching and discriminating abilities of parasite and host, respectively, are good examples of such an 'arms race' in birds. In order to defend themselves from parasites, many hosts have evolved discriminating abilities that allow them to recognize and reject imposter eggs in their nests. In response, parasites have evolved a counter-strategy, whereby they closely match their eggs with those of their hosts. In turn, the hosts evolved a counter-counter strategy of changing their egg patterning, and cuckoos countered this by tracking the changes – and so this ongoing evolutionary arms race continues to play itself out. This phenomenon is also known as 'co-evolution' whereby the changes in one species are a direct response to the changes that have occurred in another.

LINES OF DEFENCE

The ability of the host to distinguish foreign eggs from those of its own is one example of a defence against brood parasitism. Another is to simply abandon the parasitized clutch. However, hosts have evolved other means of defending themselves.

No entry

An interesting defence against brood parasitsm is employed by the Lesser Masked-Weaver, which is parasitized by the Diderick Cuckoo. The weaver is slightly smaller than the cuckoo, and builds its distinctive nest with its entrance tunnel pointing downwards. It has been observed that the female cuckoo often struggles to fit through the tunnel entrance. Nests have been found with a female cuckoo so firmly wedged in the entrance tube that she has been unable to escape and has died there. It has been suggested that the Lesser Masked-Weaver has, in recent years, narrowed the diameter of the entrance tunnel to their nests, and may be on the way to winning the latest round in their battle with the cuckoos.

Safety in numbers

Some hosts, such as the Southern Red Bishop, appear to have evolved a means of preventing cuckoos from even approaching their nests. Since

The Southern Red Bishop nests in colonies where individuals often group together to repel parasites.

they nest in colonies, the bishops have the advantage of multiple lookouts who will spot any cuckoo attempting to 'infiltrate' the colony. Once a cuckoo is spotted nearby, the bishops 'gang up' and aggressively mob and chase the intruder until it leaves. Because of this, larger colonies of bishops tend to have far fewer incidents of brood parasitism than smaller ones. Although this is not the only reason that Southern Red Bishops breed in colonies, there are compelling arguments to suggest that one good reason for doing so could be to counteract cuckoo parasitism.

Song

Some birds are thought to use song as a means of defence against brood parasitism. For example, the Chorister Robin-Chat, with an extensive mimicking repertoire, often imitates the call of the parasitic African Emerald Cuckoo. Although this theory is untested, it has been proposed that, with this call, the robin-chat may repel real cuckoos by giving the impression that there is already another territorial cuckoo in the area, thereby making local nests less vulnerable to brood parasitism.

RETAINING A SENSE OF IDENTITY

It's a mystery as to why brood parasite chicks, which are raised by a totally different species, do not suffer from an 'identity crisis', but recognize and know to associate with birds of their own species once they are independent. Such chicks' sense of identity is clearly genetic, and their ability to recognize both the appearance and song of their own species is inherited. In this case, the adult parasite will not respond to the songs of its foster parent but rather to those of its own species.

By contrast, an interesting example of the opposite effect is found among indigobirds, where each of the four species

parasitizes a specific firefinch or twinspot host. Different indigobird species look remarkably similar, the males differing only by the sheen on their feathers and the colour of their bill and legs, while the females are also almost impossible to distinguish in the field. They are most easily distinguished by elements of their song – each male indigobird species mimics the call of its specific firefinch host, which it learns and imprints on while being reared. In the same way, female indigobirds, although they themselves don't sing, also learn to recognize their host's song. This enables the females to recognize mates of the same species, as well as allowing them to identify, by their song, the correct host nest in which to lay. Locating precisely the correct firefinch host is vital as it ensures that young parasite chicks' mouth markings will closely resemble those of the host's chicks' specific markings, critical if they are to be accepted and reared by the host.

This Village Indigobird parasitizes the Red-billed Firefinch. The adults accurately mimic the song of the hosts, while the chicks' gape markings mimic the distinctive markings of the host chicks' gapes.

BROOD PARASITISM IN AFRICAN CUCKOOS, SHOWING THE DIFFERENT TACTICS USED BY EACH SPECIES.

SPECIES	MONOGAMOUS/ PROMISCUOUS	NUMBER OF HOSTS	MATCHING EGGS (*)	REMOVES HOST'S EGGS	REMOVES HOST'S CHICKS	CHICK EVICTS CHICKS
African Cuckoo	P	1	*	*		*
Red-chested Cuckoo	P	>17		*	*	*
Black Cuckoo	P	4	*	*		
Levaillant's Cuckoo	M	10	*			*
Jacobin Cuckoo	M	>16		*		*
Thick-billed Cuckoo	P	1	*			
Great Spotted Cuckoo	P	>1	*		*	
Diederik Cuckoo	P	>18			*	*
Klaas's Cuckoo	P	>24	*		*	*
African Emerald Cuckoo	M	>3	*			

A Cape Robin-Chat feeds a Red-chested Cuckoo.

9 SONGS AND SOUNDS

An African Fish-Eagle pair calling together

WHAT DOES BIRD SONG MEAN? Ornithologists have been trying to interpret the complex and subtle musical language of birds for decades. Although we will never completely understand the intricacies of what birds are 'saying', considerable progress has been made in decoding and interpreting their remarkably diverse calls and songs.

In the same way that our language is vital for communication, the varied sounds that birds make each have a specific meaning as well, from melodious harmonies to raucous cacophonies, and from stirring solo renditions to perfectly harmonized duets and group symphonies. Indeed, bird calls are among birds' most distinctive features, enabling us to identify a species by its call alone.

MUSIC WITH MEANING

A bird's musical language is remarkably expressive and versatile. It is used as an acoustic 'weapon' to challenge and intimidate opponents, as a vocal beacon to proclaim territory, as a romantic ballad to entice and woo mates, as an effective alarm system to warn chicks of impending danger and as a contact call to keep in touch with other birds of its species.

Staking out a territory

The male bird often uses song to proclaim his territory and express his social standing. He usually sings persistently from a conspicuous perch, advertising his position to rival males. It is thought that by singing continually from a number of places within the same area, he establishes the boundaries of the territory. If an unfamiliar stranger calls within a bird's territory, or is spotted within it, the male responds immediately by singing more loudly and more persistently, and will often aggressively approach and chase away the rival male.

Swainson's Spurfowl in full cry, declaring its territory.

CALLS VERSUS SONGS

Strictly, bird vocalizations can be classified as either calls or songs. Calls are usually described as simple sounds made by both male and female throughout the year, and include contact calls between individuals, warning calls to alert others of danger, and begging calls by hungry young to attract the attention of their parents. In contrast, songs are generally longer and more melodious, and are usually performed only by the male in territorial display and defence, and for attracting mates. True song is usually found only in the so-called 'songbirds', which are the most accomplished of songsters. However, researchers question the validity of these definitions, as the distinction between songs and calls is often unclear.

THE 'BEAU GESTE' EFFECT

It is thought that territorial males give the impression that there is more than just one bird in the area by calling from different places within their territory and using a number of different songs. This has become known as the 'Beau Geste' effect, after a novel by the same name that describes a tactic used by soldiers of the Foreign Legion, who propped up dead soldiers in bunkers to fool the enemy into thinking that the area was well defended.

A musical aphrodisiac

In addition to being a territorial proclamation, a male bird's song may also come across as a romantic serenade when heard by a passing female. While in some species a male's song may be interpreted by a rival male as an ominous threat to 'keep out', the same song, or a subtle variation of it, could be an enticing invitation for a female to 'come in'.

Once a female bird is attracted to the alluring song of the male and accepts him as a worthy partner, a pair bond is usually formed. He then needs to maintain the liaison and keep her in his territory, and one way of doing so is by continuing to serenade her. The familiar sound of male robin-chats singing melodiously from the undergrowth is a good example of this. Many groups of birds have distinctive displays accompanying their vocalizations, such as larks, bishops and widowbirds. Male Southern Red Bishops and Long-tailed Widowbirds have characteristic flight displays over their nesting territories with fluffed plumage and a series of rapid calls (*see* Chapter 4, page 61).

A Bokmakierie sings from a conspicuous perch.

An expression of identity

Vocalizations are important signals that birds use to express both their individual and species identity. Although other factors such as appearance and behaviour also help birds to recognize others of their species, sounds are decisive. For this reason, sounds are often taken into consideration when scientists classify (or re-classify) species. They are particularly valuable when trying to distinguish between different species of birds whose appearance and behaviour are very similar (the cisticolas, for example) or those in a single species whose appearance varies greatly throughout their distribution (as in the case of numerous lark species, for example).

The melodious song of the male Rufous-naped Lark compensates for its drab appearance.

In some cases, songs and calls can be an expression of a bird's individual identity. Although the basic structure of the song or call of each species is fairly standard and distinctive, in some species each bird develops its own subtly individual song. While other members of the species might recognize the particular style of an individual bird, we would usually require the song to be plotted on a sonogram to detect its particularity. This individual recognition is important in a number of situations: the quality of a male's song is often one of the criteria used by a female to assess a potential mate and choose one over another. It is also important for territorial males to be able to recognize a new song, belonging to a potential rival. In addition, it allows mates to recognize both each other and their chicks – particularly important in birds such as gannets, which nest in vast colonies and return to a sea of feathered faces.

Sounding the alarm

Most birds instinctively 'sound the alarm' in response to danger, using specific alarm calls to do this. Interestingly, unlike most calls which are only recognized and responded to by birds of the same species, alarm calls seem to act as an almost universal signal among passerines. This may create a frenzy of agitated behaviour, as several species of birds group together to mob and aggressively chase away an intruder such as a snake, mongoose or raptor. Alarm calls warning of aerial predators are often long, high-frequency hisses, the source of which is difficult to pinpoint. For slow-moving predators such as snakes, the alarm call is a clearer one and is easier to locate. Although it is unusual for birds of different species to work together, group mobbings do take place when there is a greater chance of chasing away a predator if all the species in the area co-operate. Chicks also instinctively know to react to the alarm calls given by their parents – a vital survival mechanism.

Staying in touch

Birds have a number of different contact calls that are a vital means of staying in touch with one another in a range of circumstances. Birds that live and forage in thick bush, like the Terrestrial Brownbul, Arrow-marked Babbler and Cape White-eye, make constant use of contact calls in order to keep the flock together. Some birds that migrate during the night in flocks, such as bee-eaters, warblers,

A sandgrouse chick crouches motionless when the adult sounds the alarm.

A young Olive Thrush's persistent begging attracts the attention of its parent (RIGHT).

swifts, geese and many waders, rely on a continuous stream of contact calls as an essential means of keeping in touch with one another in the dark. In most species, contact calls are also an important means for adults to locate their chicks.

Begging calls

In order to be fed, chicks need to be noticed. This is most effectively achieved by incessant calling, accompanied by frantic wing shaking. Begging calls are found mainly in altricial chicks that are born naked and helpless and rely on their parents to bring them food. In contrast, the precocial chicks of most ground-nesting species are relatively independent and feed themselves soon after hatching. They also use contact calls more often than altricial chicks.

THE SYRINX: A WELL-TUNED INSTRUMENT

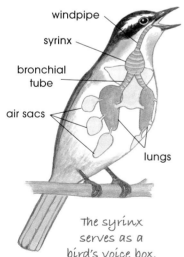

windpipe

syrinx

bronchial tube

air sacs

lungs

The syrinx serves as a bird's voice box.

Unlike humans, birds do not have vocal chords to produce sound, nor do they use their tongue and mouth to help them create sounds as we do. Instead, they have a specialized sound-producing organ called the syrinx, which is equivalent to our larynx or voice box. However, unlike the human larynx, which is at the top of the windpipe, in birds the syrinx is at the bottom, where the bronchial tubes (one coming from each lung) meet, giving it two different sources of air. Musical sounds are produced when air is forced over the vibrating membranes of the syrinx from the air sacs and lungs. By varying the size of the syrinx openings and the length of the windpipe, birds are able to control the pitch and quality of the sound produced.

Interestingly, some birds are able to produce two completely different sounds at the same time – one from each side of the syrinx. The air from the lungs and air sacs on one side of the body produces a sound of different pitch and quality to the air from the other side of the body. Another fascinating adaptation is the ability of some birds, such as the Crested Barbet, to call for an incredibly long period without stopping to take a breath. They achieve this continuous note by expelling air from each side of the syrinx consecutively.

LEARNED OR INHERITED?

Do birds instinctively know how to sing, or do they first have to undergo some form of 'voice training' before becoming accomplished songsters?

Song development in about half of all species is now thought to be a combination of instinct and learning. Most birds are born with an instinctive ability to recognize and produce the basic structure of their species' particular song. However, it is by listening to, learning from and imitating the songs of their parents and other birds of the same species that they gradually refine and master their individual song, which will be used in territorial and courtship displays when they are older.

For the Southern Boubou chick (LEFT) song is acquired through both instinct and learning, while for the Klaas's Cuckoo chick (RIGHT) song is purely inherited.

BIRDS THAT ARE HEARD BUT NOT SEEN

As numerous frustrated birders will testify, many birds are highly elusive, often revealing their presence only by their distinctive calls. Skulking waterbirds such as crakes, flufftails, bitterns and rails are notorious for being so elusive that they are invariably heard rather than seen, while the distinctive 'Piet-my-vrou' song of the Red-chested Cuckoo is more familiar than sightings of the bird itself. The nocturnal nightjars are also generally heard before they are seen.

The distinctive calls of different species sharing a similar rather drab, non-descript appearance are often an important aid in their identification. What these species, such as warblers, larks and cisticolas, may lack in appearance, however, they more than make up for in song, relying on sound rather than appearance to communicate with and impress mates.

The African Rail is invariably heard rather than seen.

This song learning usually occurs during a sensitive period of the imprinting stage, when birds memorize the sounds that they hear. In species such as cuckoos, on the other hand, which are not raised by their own parents and only hear the vocalizations of their foster parents, song must be solely inherited.

Calls, on the other hand, such as warning, alarm and contact calls, which are generally more basic in structure than songs, are thought to be instinctive.

A SYMPHONY OF SOUNDS

Musical maestros that they are, many birds show a flair for impressively accomplished singing repertoires, while others draw on a variety of avian 'instruments' to communicate creatively and effectively.

Duets

Whereas in most species males try to woo the females with a solo performance, in a number of bird species both male and female sing together in a perfectly synchronized duet. The co-ordination of the two songs is timed so precisely that it is often difficult to distinguish that the sound is actually coming from two birds and not one.

Some birds, such as the Black-collared Barbet, sing their duets sitting close beside each other on a branch. Their performance is so well dove-tailed that although each individual call lasts a mere fraction of a second, their combined call is in perfect rhythm. Although not as well co-ordinated as the barbet, other well known practitioners of the duet include the Brubru, tchagras, bush-shrikes, helmet-shrikes and batises.

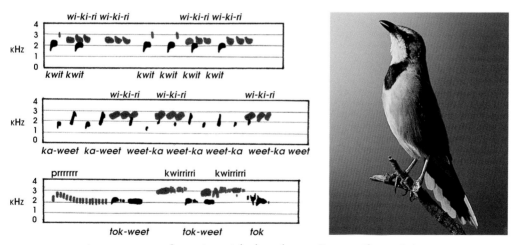

A sonogram of a Bokmakierie pair's well co-ordinated duet

Many duetting birds live in thick vegetation, so the singers are often out of sight of each other. A duet is thus thought to be a musical, rather than a visual, means of helping to reinforce and maintain the pair bond. This is especially important in duetting birds, as they are usually monogamous and stay together for a number of years. Because they are usually resident rather than migratory, and maintain a territory all year round, the often strident duet is also thought to be an important means of proclaiming the pair's territory to rivals.

The Southern Boubou's song varies from area to area.

Dialects

As with humans, where different dialects may develop in populations that are geographically separated from each other, so too do dialects evolve in bird populations. For example, a Southern Boubou in the Western Cape in South Africa may sing very differently from a Southern Boubou in Mpumalanga Province. Many dialects are very subtle and, although recognized by birds, would not always be detected by our ears. We would need to examine sonograms of the particular species in order to see the different patterns.

There is some debate as to whether these different dialects actually play a specific role in communication, or whether they have merely resulted from birds learning slight variations in song in different areas. The fact that different dialects are found in populations in different areas, and that these areas are often separated by a geographical barrier, such as a large mountain range, implies that, over time, there would be very little, if any, gene flow between the populations. In addition, because song is so important for birds of the same species to recognize each other, it is likely that females of a specific population would choose only males that sing a familiar dialect as mates. These factors have led scientists to believe that, with time, all populations with specific dialects could eventually diverge and develop into totally new species.

An example illustrating this is the case of the Clapper Lark, which has recently been split into three species: the Eastern Clapper, Cape Clapper and Agulhas Clapper larks. Among the criteria used in splitting this group were the variations in their song and differing wing-clapping displays.

Mimicry

Most birders have been fooled by an accomplished bird mimic singing the song of another species. These birds' repertoires may consist almost entirely of calls and sounds copied from other birds. Well-known mimics include chats, drongos, robin-chats, larks, bulbuls, shrikes, white-eyes, indigobirds and starlings.

How and why mimicry has evolved in birds is a conundrum as, in theory, it would seem to make life more confusing for birds. A possible explanation is that this ability in males could be a signal of their fitness, and increase their chances of both intimidating other males and attracting females.

The plucky Fork-tailed Drongo is a well-known bird mimic, accurately duplicating the calls of a number of different species.

In the case of certain brood parasites, the advantages of mimicry are more obvious. For example, indigobirds have evolved a close relationship with various species of firefinches, whose nests they parasitize. The indigobird chicks learn and later mimic the hosts' song, presumably allowing adult indigobirds to locate both one another and the nests of the firefinch species they parasitize (*see* Chapter 8, page 116).

Song repertoires

In many species of birds, the males are true vocal virtuosos in the breeding season, not restricting themselves to one song only but displaying an impressive repertoire of different songs. The advantage to birds of having evolved such long and varied song repertoires has been much debated, and two main explanations have been put forward: First, it is thought that males with larger song repertoires are able to acquire and defend territories of a higher quality than males with fewer songs, their singing ability being a strong vocal signal to other males of their superiority. Second, it has been shown that birds with larger song repertoires are able to impress and attract more females. For both these reasons, it is likely that musical versatility gives males a significant advantage in breeding.

The White-browed Robin-Chat is a true avian virtuoso and has a wide song repertoire, as illustrated by these different sonograms.

An avian orchestra

Many birds make use of a range of more unusual 'avian instruments' to produce sounds that either complement their songs and calls, or are used alone.

Certain birds use their bills like a pair of Spanish castanets to produce a distinctive sound known as **bill-snapping.** Bill-snapping is characteristic of the shrike family (helmetshrikes, Black-backed Puffback, Brubru, bush-shrikes, batises), and is used extensively in their mating displays. It is also one of the few sounds made by many stork species, which are otherwise quite laconic creatures. The Marabou Stork frequently uses bill-snapping in both nuptial and threat displays, creating a loud, hollow-sounding rattling noise.

Marabou Storks use bill-snapping to communicate in mating or threat displays.

Wing-clapping is characteristic of the Flappet and three species of Clapper larks, which produce the unusual sound by rapidly beating the tips of their wings together during their aerial mating display. The frequency and length of the strenuous, high-energy clapping bout is thought to be a signal to females of the male's fitness, and therefore his potential as a good mate. The Wing-snapping Cisticola, as its name so aptly implies, makes extensive use of wing-snapping during the dramatic vertical dive at the end of its mating display, as well as when alarmed or agitated.

HABITAT AND SONG

Song is particularly important for birds living in thick, wooded habitats, where sound rather than sight is the predominant form of communication. Because thick vegetation influences the distance that calls can travel and may also distort the original sound, the calls of these birds generally consist of loud, repeated notes, and are simple in structure. Examples of such birds include many barbets and cuckoos. Also, low-pitched sounds travel better than higher ones through dense vegetation. The Eurasian Bittern, for example, which lives in thick reed-beds, produces a deep, resonant, booming noise, which probably gives it the long distance record in sound transmission for a bird call (up to 5 km).

In contrast, birds living in open habitats usually have more complex songs with a larger repertoire. Larks, for instance, which are typically terrestrial and live in open grassland and tree savannah, often have elaborate calls that are not at risk of becoming distorted.

The African Snipe uses another idiosyncratic sound to impress potential mates and ward off competitors – that of **tail drumming**. By fanning and 'fripping' its outer tail feathers during a dramatic diving display over its territory, the male snipe produces a resonating drumming sound lasting two to five seconds.

Avian 'Morse code'

In much the same way that rhythmic drumbeats were once used by humans to communicate with one another over long distances, so too do wood- peckers use their strong, chisel-like bills to hammer out a rapid pattern of sounds on hard, resonant surfaces such as dead tree trunks. This drumming ability enables them to communicate by beating out characteristic and meaningful sig- nals. Of the southern African species, the Bearded Woodpecker has the loudest tapping pattern.

The Bearded Woodpecker has developed its own form of Morse code, com- municating over great distances by drumming loudly on dead tree trunks.

Not only does each species of woodpecker have its own distinct drum pattern, but each bird also has its own subtle drumming signature that can be used to identify individuals. This avian 'Morse code' seems to carry a strong message to woodpeckers of the same species – a bold territorial proclamation as well as a courtship rhythm used during the breeding season. Territorial drumming can be distinguished from that of chiselling for food, as it follows a specific pattern, whereas the sounds caused by hammering for food are more haphazard.

THE DAWN CHORUS

Birders soon find out that there is one time of the day that is particularly good for birding: the early morning. This is a time when many species show a peak in singing activity, and call together in what sounds like an unrehearsed yet accomplished choir. There are three main theories as to why birds sing so actively at dawn:

The **reception is clearer.** Sound is known to carry up to 20 times more effectively at dawn because conditions are generally calmer in the early morning compared to later in the day. Because of this, birds make the most use of these favourable conditions for communication. Sound is also known to travel better in clear conditions and on hot days than in cold, cloudy weather.

Often, **feeding conditions are not ideal at dawn,** with low light conditions at this early hour making it more difficult for birds to hunt by sight, especially for insects. In addition, invertebrate prey is generally less active, and more difficult to find, in the cool dawn. For this reason singing becomes the favoured activity.

Dawn is often the time that any **vacant territories first become apparent,** so this is when invading males would be most likely to secure an available territory. At the start of a new day, males may also sing with renewed gusto to reconnect with their mate in order to maintain the pair bond.

INTERPRETING SONOGRAMS

It can be quite daunting when first trying to identify a bird by its call. However, if interpreted carefully, sonograms can help to illustrate at least three important aspects of a bird-call or song: (a) **frequency** (pitch) of a call can be deduced by the vertical height of the tracing on the sonogram – the higher the tracing extends, the higher the frequency; (b) **duration** (length) of the call is simply the horizontal length of the tracing, and (c) **amplitude** (volume) of the call is reflected in the darkness of the tracing, from grey (quiet) to black (loud).

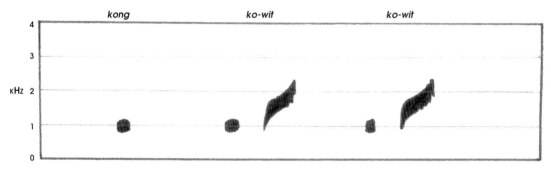

The pure, clear song of the Gorgeous Bush-Shrike is
reflected in the distinct, low-frequency tracings.

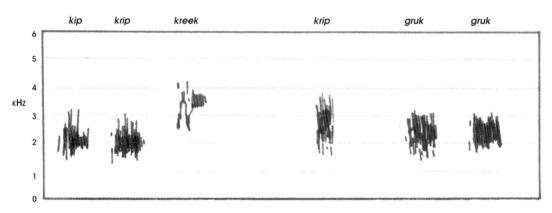

The harsh, grating sound of the Great Reed-Warbler can be seen in
the close-set vertical lines, which cover a wide range of frequencies.

Qualities such as tone and rhythm are also reflected in sonograms. Souds with a pure tone, such as those of the Emerald-spotted Wood-Dove and Gorgeous Bush-Shrike, have a narrow frequency range (a short vertical height on the tracing). In contrast, the harsh, nasal calls of birds like the Greater Blue-eared Starling and the Great Reed-Warbler, are shorter, cover a wide range of frequencies and appear as vertical lines.

Rhythm can be detected by the speed and length of the tracing. For example, short notes make short tracings (e.g. Scop's Owl), while long notes make long tracings (e.g. Red-billed Oxpecker).

Onomatopoeia in birds

The sounds of some bird names are remarkably descriptive of the actual call the bird makes. For example:

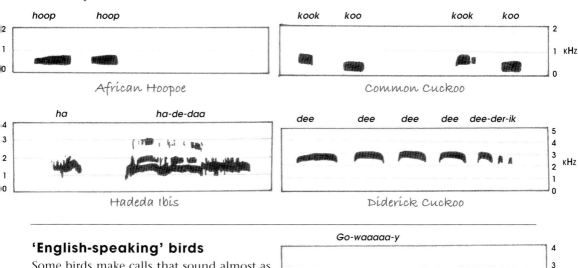

African Hoopoe

Common Cuckoo

Hadeda Ibis

Diderick Cuckoo

'English-speaking' birds

Some birds make calls that sound almost as though they were speaking the language of the listening human, and have come to be described using these phrases. Once one recognizes one of these calls, it becomes almost impossible to forget the phrase. Some examples of birds calling in 'English' are:

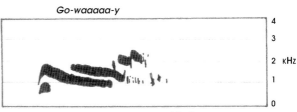

Grey Go-away-bird

Monotonous Lark
For syrup is sweet

Shelley's Francolin
I'll drink your beer

White-browed Robin-Chat
Don't you do it

African Emerald Cuckoo
Pretty Georgie

Emerald-spotted Wood-Dove
My mother is dead, my father is dead and I'm sad sad sad sad

Black Cuckoo
I'm so sad

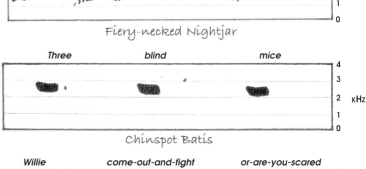

Fiery-necked Nightjar

Chinspot Batis

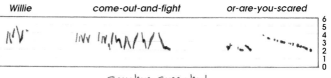

Sombre Greenbul

DID YOU KNOW?

▮ The Natal Francolin is known as the suicide bird for scaring people senseless with its raucous call when flushed.

▮ The Trumpeter Hornbill's call sounds like the cry of a young baby.

▮ The African Rail emits a shrill, trilling rattle that is usually the only notification of its presence.

▮ The call of the Cape Longclaw sounds like a cat's 'meow'.

▮ The Neddicky is commonly known as the 'typewriting' bird, owing to its call.

▮ The Blacksmith Lapwing is named for its distinctive call, which sounds like a blacksmith striking his hammer on an anvil.

▮ The Burchell's Coucal is called the 'rainbird', as it often calls before, during or after rain, emitting a series of rapid hooting notes that sound like water bubbling out of a narrow-necked bottle.

African Scops-Owl

Burchell's Coucal

▮ The diminutive African Scops-Owl emits a high-pitched ventriloquist-like purring call, sometimes repeated up to 40 times.

▮ The shrikes have a variety of familiar calls, from the mournful, monotonous call of the 'spookvoël' (ghost bird) or Grey-headed Bush-shrike to the melodious whistling song of the Orange-breasted Bush-Shrike and the bell-like, liquid, five-syllabled call of the Gorgeous Bush-Shrike. The Black-backed Puffback has a distinctive clicking call used in its mating display as it puffs out its back feathers, hence the Afrikaans name 'sneeubal' (snowball).

▮ An interesting adaptation occurs in the case of the reverberating, booming calls of the African Snipe and Kori Bustard. A sac connected to the oesophagus can be filled with air to be used as a chamber in their vocal displays.

10 BIRD MENUS

A Woodland Kingfisher in typical display pose offers a frog to its mate as a nuptial gift.

BIRDS EXPLOIT ALMOST EVERY AVAILABLE FOOD SOURCE ON THE PLANET.
From hard seeds to succulent plants, rich nectar to soft wax, writhing insects to microscopic plankton and scaled fish to rotting carrion – whatever the food source, some species of bird will eat it. To do so, birds have evolved highly specialized and often ingenious feeding techniques that allow them to peck, probe, dig, scratch, chisel or dive for their preferred food.

Birds have evolved a number of adaptations to take advantage of their varied menus. Some birds have found ways of 'chewing' their food quite effectively without the aid of teeth. Many fish-eaters have developed excellent underwater vision and an ability to hold their breath in pursuit of aquatic prey. Bee-eaters have perfected a technique to avoid getting stung by bees. A special internal storage bag allows certain birds to carry food back to their nests for their hungry chicks. Several birds, such as the oxpeckers and honeyguides, have fostered unlikely foraging relationships with other animals in order to maximize their food-gathering opportunities.

141

Nightjars have deceptively huge gapes which, together with the stiff bristles on the sides of their beaks, help them to detect and capture their insect prey.

A DIVERSITY OF DIETS

Food is so important to a bird's survival that the bird's appearance and diet usually go hand in hand – its looks are determined largely by what it puts in its stomach. The tools needed for finding food or catching prey can be seen in the shape of a bird's beak, the length of its legs, the position of its eyes, the strength of its feet, the shape of its wings and tail, and the length of its neck. The diversity in feeding methods in response to equally diverse diets allows a variety of species to live together in the same habitat, with limited competition for the same resources.

Insectivores

Insectivores eat a mixed menu of protein-rich insects as well as other invertebrates such as spiders, crustaceans, molluscs and worms. An extraordinary array of different bills are used to hunt, glean, probe or chisel for their prey. These may range from the short, slender, tweezer-like bills of warblers, to the stout, hooked bills of shrikes, the long, slender bills of bee-eaters and the probing bill of the African Hoopoe. Swifts and swallows have short bills with a wide gape, which they use for scooping up flying insects.

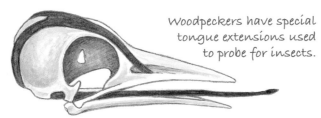

Woodpeckers have special tongue extensions used to probe for insects.

Woodpeckers are aptly named for their highly specialized habit of hammering, chiselling and prising insect larvae out from beneath the bark of trees. In addition to having a brain that is cushioned to withstand the repeated shocks of hammering, their **tongues are unique feeding tools**. The tongue has special extensions that make it exceptionally long, allowing it to reach far out beyond the tip of the bill to explore below bark and down bored insect holes. It is also covered in a sticky, glue-like mucus, and armed with fleshy barbs – a deadly combination for most insects.

White-fronted Bee-eaters are adept plucking bees from the air.

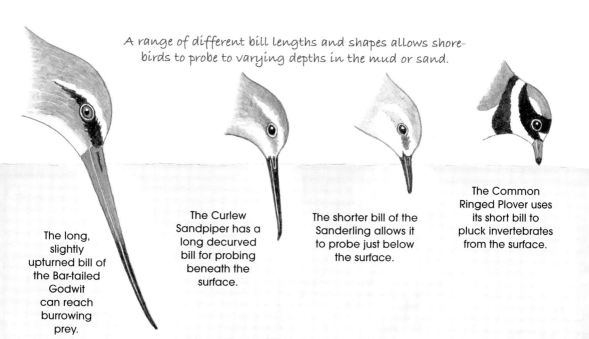

A range of different bill lengths and shapes allows shorebirds to probe to varying depths in the mud or sand.

The long, slightly upturned bill of the Bar-tailed Godwit can reach burrowing prey.

The Curlew Sandpiper has a long decurved bill for probing beneath the surface.

The shorter bill of the Sanderling allows it to probe just below the surface.

The Common Ringed Plover uses its short bill to pluck invertebrates from the surface.

The bills of different wader species vary greatly in both length and shape, allowing them to feed at different levels and on different types of food. This **allows various species to forage together**, as they are not competing for the same prey. For example, while the long, slightly upturned bill of the Bar-tailed Godwit allows it to probe deep into the mud, the Curlew Sandpiper feeds on its invertebrate prey just below the surface and the Common Ringed Plover uses its short bill to pluck prey off the surface itself.

As their name implies, bee-eaters consume bees. An intriguing question is how they manage to avoid potentially life-threatening stings. They accomplish this by vigorously rubbing each bee's abdomen against a perch, thereby **removing the sting and poison before swallowing the bee**. It is thought that even if they do get stung, bee-eaters have evolved a natural immunity against the potentially harmful toxins in bee stings. Birds are also known to be able to distinguish stingless drones from stinging workers, and have been observed swallowing drones with less caution.

Frugivores

Unlike animals, which will do anything to avoid being eaten, the opposite strategy applies to fruits – they need to be eaten, as this assists with the dispersal of their seeds. They are therefore often brightly coloured specifically to attract and entice

The African Green-Pigeon is a typical frugivore.

ORNITHOCHORY

An interesting example of a close association between a bird and a plant is that of the Yellow-fronted Tinkerbird and certain parasitic mistletoe species (e.g. *Viscum* and *Tapinantus*). The bird swallows the nutritious small fruits whole; the fleshy covering is rapidly removed in the gut in less than a minute. The bird then regurgitates the sticky seed, which is wiped off onto a branch – the perfect place for it to germinate. Because tinkerbirds need to eat over 100 fruits a day to sustain their energy requirements, the seeds are sure to be well dispersed. This mutual dependence is known as 'ornithochory', whereby certain fruit-bearing trees have become solely dependent on specific bird species for seed dispersal.

The Red-headed Finch is a typical seed-eater.

birds. Many fruit-eating birds have strong, thick, robust bills for cracking open the hard shells of fruit and cutting through tough skins. Such birds include many hornbills, barbets and parrots. Others, such as bulbuls and white-eyes, have thinner bills for eating softer fruits.

The intestine of fruit-eating birds is usually short, and the undamaged seed can sometimes pass through the gut in as little as five minutes from the time it is eaten. This ensures that the seed is dispersed a short distance from the tree but not so far away that it falls within an unsuitable habitat. Since fruits are seasonal and often occur only in specific locations, frugivores are generally gregarious and locally nomadic. Because fruits are generally deficient in protein, many frugivorous birds are known to supplement their diet with protein-rich insects.

Seed-eaters

Seeds may be very small, but they can also be extremely hard. Because of this, most seed-eaters have strong bills and jaw muscles to cope with them.

Seed-eaters can be divided into two main groups, depending on whether they husk the seed first before swallowing it, or swallow it whole. The beaks of canaries, finches and waxbills are expert husking tools. Their distinctly conical shape, with a groove and cutting edge on both the upper and lower mandibles, makes them specially adapted to husk seeds, and the bird swallows only the kernel. On the other hand,

AVIAN PEST SUPREME

One notorious seed-eater is the Red-billed Quelea, which has become an agricultural pest on cereal crops in certain areas. It is possibly the most destructive bird in the world, with flocks of up to 100 million birds being known to consume some 500 000 kg of food a day. Remarkably, the killing of some 65–180 million queleas each year during recent decades has had no obvious effect on the population, and has offered only temporary relief from crop damage.

Husker or non-husker? The Long-tailed Paradise Wydah (LEFT) has a stout, conical bill for dehusking seeds before swallowing them. The Laughing Dove's thin bill (RIGHT) is unable to husk seeds, which are swallowed whole.

seed-eaters such as doves and sandgrouse do not have beaks designed for husking. They swallow the entire seed, which is then processed in their crop and gizzard. Some sandgrouses are known to eat hundreds to thousands of these seeds a day.

The African Goshawk is a perfectly built hunting machine.

Although seeds are rich in high-energy carbohydrates, they are low in protein, so many seed-eaters usually supplement their diet with protein-rich insects. Because seeds are also low in water, most seed-eaters need to drink frequently. Sandgrouse and doves are particularly well known for their habit of congregating in large flocks at water-holes, specially in arid zones. The supplies of seeds in dry regions are particularly unpredictable and therefore seed-eaters in these regions are highly nomadic.

Raptors

Carnivorous birds of prey are aptly called 'raptors', which means 'plunderers', and is derived from the Latin *raptare* meaning to 'seize and carry away' – something they do with great skill and precision.

Each species of raptor is adapted in both its anatomy and behaviour to hunt a particular range of prey: from fish, in the case of the African Fish Eagle and Pel's Fishing-Owl, to snakes and lizards in the

A DEADLY NOTCH

Most of the smaller raptors, such as kestrels and falcons, have a sharp notch just behind the hooked bill tip. This efficient tool is used to sever the neck vertebrae of their prey, delivering a quick death. Shrikes' bills have a similar notch.

notch

Lanner Falcon

case of the Secretarybird, and small birds and mammals in the case of the accipiters and owls. Raptors usually have sharp, hooked bills for tearing meat, as well as large eyes with exceptionally keen binocular vision. They have also evolved powerful wings, sharp talons and strong muscles for killing their prey.

While some raptors hunt from a perch, others, such as falcons, hunt in the open sky. Sparrowhawks effectively hunt insects, lizards and small birds in dense bush, their broad wings allowing them to manoeuvre through the foliage. Martial Eagles have been known to catch prey as large as antelope by swooping down to grasp the prey with their powerful talons, killing it on impact.

Scavengers

Scavengers such as vultures and Marabou Storks are usually first noticed as a swirling mass of dark shapes spiralling high in the sky on rising thermals. Attractive they may not be, but they would be sorely missed if they were not around to perform the important ecological role of cleaning up after others. These scavengers have long, featherless necks, which are

White-backed Vultures and Marabou Storks are typical scavengers, sometimes spending days at a carcass.

SHRIKE LARDERS

Shrikes have a habit of impaling their prey on thorns or barbed wire fences, or jamming it into the angles of branches. Since they don't have long talons like raptors to hold their prey while it is being dismembered, impaling it helps to hold it securely. This habit is reflected in the shrikes' generic name, *Lanius*, which is Latin for 'butcher', and has given rise to the Common Fiscal's alternative name of 'butcher bird'.

The Common Fiscal or 'butcher bird' impales its prey, like this shrew, on a branch or fence.

perfect for thrusting deep into a carcass. Because they make use of food that is normally scarce and scattered, they have evolved the ability to roam widely and survey large areas in search of a meal, and catching thermals is a low-energy means of doing this.

When vultures arrive to feed at a carcass, there is generally an accepted hierarchy or **pecking order** that determines proceedings. First at the scene is usually the large, heavily built Lappet-faced Vulture, which flies at relatively low altitudes in search of food. Its role is to sever the carcass with its massive bill and get at the bowels. This is the most aggressive and powerful of the vultures and it often keeps other species at bay. It is usually followed by the White-headed Vulture, which also has a powerful bill that it uses for twisting and tearing meat from the bones.

White-backed Vultures, which soar at high levels, normally spot the carcass from the air by watching the movements of other vultures and often descend on the carcass in huge numbers. Their tongues have backward-facing spines, which aid in tugging meat from the bones. A White-backed Vulture can fill its crop in just two minutes. Finally, the much smaller Hooded Vultures arrive, and use their narrower bills to peck scattered fragments or pick at the scraps left on the bones.

The Marabou Stork is another familiar scavenger at a kill, and gets its name from the French word *marabout* meaning 'an ugly, misshapen old man'. Because their bills are not adapted for tearing meat from a carcass, they often **shadow the vultures** and steal pieces of meat that they have torn off. These large birds are able to gulp down pieces of meat weighing up to 600 g, and are sometimes known to wash these chunks in water before swallowing them!

Piracy on the open ocean is quite common. Although lacking eye patches, peg legs and parrots on their shoulders, avian pirates roam the seas on the lookout for nutritious bounty. While many pelagic birds such as petrels, skuas and sheathbills have scavenging habits, feeding mostly on dead seals and penguins, some, such as skuas and tropicbirds, are also known to steal prey from other species such as gulls, gannets and terns. They viciously chase, terrorize and molest their victims until they drop their food in order to get away. Such 'piracy' also occurs among certain raptors.

'Gone fishing'

Although fish are highly nutritious and rich in protein, they are a challenge to catch: in addition to living in water, they are fast-moving and slippery. To overcome these obstacles, birds have evolved an array of fishing techniques and adaptations to capture their elusive prey, from waiting, watching, stabbing, trawling and chasing, to diving, swooping and grabbing. These fishing methods might require, among other talents, infinite patience, exceptional stealth, speed and accuracy.

Because these different fishing techniques are too numerous to cover in detail, the most important and fascinating adaptations for each method have been high-lighted below, and an avian practitioner named in each instance.

TRAWLING – White Pelican

- This bird has an extremely flexible lower jaw that allows the pouch to expand into a large, bowl-shaped bag.
- Its bill can hold more food than its entire stomach.
- The large gular pouch is used as a fishing net.
- They often fish in large groups, herding shoals of fish in front of them.
- Fish and water are caught in the pouch, and the water expelled before the fish are swallowed.

UNDERWATER PURSUIT – African Penguin

- A transparent 'third eyelid' allows it to see under water. Unlike most flying birds, it has heavy bones that reduce buoyancy.
- As an adaptation to diving, it has lost the use of its external nostrils and breathes through the corners of its mouth.
- Paddle-like wings allow it to 'fly' through the water, while webbed feet act as rudders.
- Barb-like spines on the tongue and palate enable it to secure slippery prey before swallowing.
- It can remain underwater for up to 20 minutes; usually dives to a depth of 10–30 m, but can reach depths of up to 120 m.

UNDERWATER STABBER – African Darter

- Its neck vertebrae and muscles have evolved to form an effective speargun-like 'trigger mechanism' that darts the bill swiftly at underwater prey.
- A transparent 'third eyelid' allows it to see underwater.
- Its bones do not have airspaces like those of most birds, reducing its buoyancy.
- Its feathers are not water resistant and therefore don't trap a layer of air between them, allowing it to submerge more easily
- It harpoons fish with its bill slightly open, returns to the surface and tosses it up, catching the fish in its beak and then swallowing it head first.
- It dives at a depth of up to 6 m.
- Its feet are webbed and far back on the body, an adaptation for swimming.
- It is sometimes referred to as the 'snake bird', due to the snake-like shape of its neck as it swims low in the water.

FISHING FROM A PERCH – African Fish Eagle and Pel's Fishing-Owl

- Their naked legs and the roughened or spiky soles of their feet help to hold slippery fish.
- They swoop from their perch to snatch fish from the surface of the water.
- They have broad wings for carrying heavy prey.

HOVER-AND-DIVE – Pied Kingfisher

- It is able to correct for the refraction that causes the illusory displacement of fish in the water, and is also able to make sudden adjustments for any last-minute movement by fish.
- It has a long, straight, sharp bill for catching fish.
- Prey is grabbed with the bill tip, taken to a perch and beaten to immobilize it before it is swallowed.

FISHING IN FLIGHT – Cape Gannet

- It is able to plunge to considerable depths by opening and retracting its wings just before striking the water. This creates a streamlined shape and allows it to plummet deep into the water.
- It has a network of air sacs beneath the skin that act as shock absorbers to soften the impact when diving. Feathers covering its body and head also form a dense, cushioning layer.
- It has lost the use of its nostrils (an adaptation for plunge diving) and breathes instead through the sides of the bill.
- Huge flocks dive from a height for shoals of fish.

STAND-AND-WAITERS VERSUS STALK-AND-STABBERS

- 'Stand-and-waiters' such as the Goliath Heron wait motionless in the water and swiftly grab fish that move within striking distance.
- The Green-backed Heron is occasionally known to use bait, placing an insect on the water surface and waiting for a fish to bite.
- 'Stalk-and-stabbers' such as the Little Egret and Hamerkop walk slowly through shallow water, waiting for the slightest movement from potential prey, then stabbing it with their sharp beaks, or grabbing it.
- They have long legs for wading.
- They spread their toes to prevent them sinking into the mud.
- They have long, sharp bills for grabbing fish.
- Their long necks enable them to reach prey underwater.

SWALLOWED HEAD FIRST

To avoid a potentially life-threatening mishap, fish-eating birds have to swallow their prey the right way round: head first. This ensures that the scales, fins and tail are facing the right way so the fish slips down easily – tail first it might get stuck.

A Malachite Kingfisher prepares to swallow a fish head first.

Nectarivore tongues are usually deeply grooved or tubular, often with a feathered tip, an adaptation for accessing nectar.

to the next. It is thought that the reciprocal relationship that has evolved between certain plants and nectarivorous birds (known as co-evolution) is so close that in rare cases they are totally dependent on each other for their survival

Sunbirds and sugarbirds are specially adapted to feeding on nectar, with long, thin bills that are able to probe into nectarous flowers. Sunbirds have exceptionally long tongues that enable them to reach far beyond the bill tip, allowing them to extract nectar from particularly long, curved flowers. These tongues are usually deeply grooved or tubular for drawing up nectar,

Nectarivores

Flowering plants and their avian pollinators have a reciprocal relationship that benefits both parties. While feeding on nectar, birds are at the same time fulfilling the important function of pollinating the flowers. Pollen often sticks to the bird's breast, head, throat or beak, and is thus carried from one flower

A Southern Double-collared Sunbird with orchid pollinaria firmly stuck to its bill.

The Scarlet-chested Sunbird is an efficient nectar feeder.

and have a special brush-like tip. Certain sunbirds also have flaps of skin over their nostrils that are thought to help keep pollen out.

If the flower is too long, birds may sometimes puncture the base of the flower with their bills to reach the nectar. This habit is known as 'nectar robbing' as the birds are essentially stealing precious nectar without 'paying' the plant for it through pollination.

While nectar is the staple diet of birds such as sunbirds and sugarbirds, other species such as barbets, bulbuls, orioles, starlings, white-eyes, weavers and canaries feed on nectar as a 'side dish', but do not rely on it for their everyday food needs.

Although nectar is very high in carbohydrates, it is low in protein, so nectar-feeding birds often need to complement their diet with insects and other small invertebrates.

LIFE–SAVING SALT GLANDS

If it were not for a special adaptation, the lament 'water, water everywhere, nor any drop to drink' of the desparate sailor in Samuel Taylor Coleridge's *The Rime of the Ancient Mariner* could very well be shared by many seabirds. These birds are surrounded by seawater that has such a high salt content that drinking it actually causes greater thirst and can lead to serious dehydration. To cope with their dangerously high salt intake, both from the seawater and from their food, these birds have evolved a special survival strategy: salt-secreting glands. The salt glands lie either above or just in front of the eye, and are able to remove salt efficiently from the bloodstream. The glands lead into the nasal cavity; the salty liquid is either shaken or 'sneezed' out of the nostrils. In diving birds such as gannets, pelicans and penguins, which have non-functional nostrils, salt is excreted into the mouth.

THE BLACK UMBRELLA

The Black Heron has evolved its own highly specialized fishing method by casting an umbrella-like shadow over the water with its wings spread. It is thought that this has the dual purpose of helping to shade its eyes from the glare of the sun, as well as attracting fish to the shady spot created underwater.

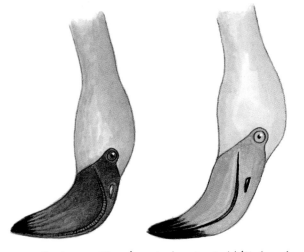

The Lesser Flamingo's deep-keeled bill (LEFT) filters minute blue-green algae and diatoms from the water, while the Greater Flamingo's shallow-keeled bill (RIGHT) has coarser filters to strain small invertebrates.

Filter feeders

Birds such as flamingos, ducks and prions have built-in sieves along the sides of their bills. These are called 'lamellae' and are an adaptation for straining fine particles of food out of the water.

Flamingos have one of the most distinctive and specialized of all avian bills. They have a large, troughlike lower mandible with a powerful, fleshy tongue that pumps water through the bill as it is held upside down in the water. The Greater Flamingo has coarse filters that enable it to sieve small invertebrates such as shrimps, insects and larvae from muddy water stirred up by its feet. By contrast, the Lesser Flamingo has a much finer filter, which it uses to sieve minute blue-green algae and diatoms. Because the two flamingo species feed on such different types of food, they do not compete with each other and so are often found feeding together.

Flamingos are highly gregarious, congregating in enormous flocks. It has been estimated that the total Lesser Flamingo population of East Africa consumes about 550 tons of blue-green algae every day.

DIGESTING THE MEAL

While their lack of teeth certainly helps to make birds lighter, it does come with a limitation: they cannot chew their food before swallowing it. Because of this, the bird's digestive system, in particular the crop and the specialized stomach, has evolved to process unchewed food.

The crop: an effective food storage bag

When birds swallow their food, it enters a specialized food storage chamber known as the crop. The crop or, in birds without a crop, the proventriculus, softens the food and controls its flow through the digestive tract. This storage capacity allows birds to swallow much more food than they would otherwise be able to at one sitting. A raptor's full crop is sometimes so large that it appears like a bulbous growth on its neck. The crop also enables adults to store and carry food back to their nests for their chicks.

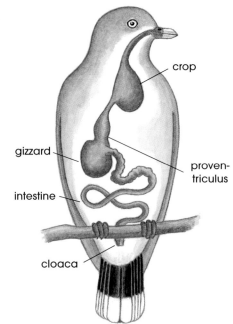

A bird's digestive system includes a proventriculus, crop and gizzard.

JOINING THE PARTY

When birding one sometimes comes across lively aggregations of birds of different species, all feeding together in a loose flock. These are known as 'bird parties'. For solitary birds that do not live in protective flocks, joining other species may increase their chances of survival as there are more birds on the lookout for danger, and therefore more time can be focused on foraging. Feeding in a flock may also improve a bird's chances of finding food, as one species may disturb insects that are only eaten by another. Different species may also feed at slightly different levels, using different foraging techniques, and usually specialize in different kinds of prey. As the birds are not in direct competition with one another, joining the party has many benefits.

This Crowned Eagle has a bulging crop after eating a large meal.

The gizzard: chewing without teeth

In a sense, birds have transferred their teeth from their jaws to a more appropriate position: that of their two-part stomach. The food is first 'chewed' through a process of chemical mastication by strong digestive juices in the upper stomach (proventriculus). It then passes into the specialized muscular gizzard, which is lined with many hard, tooth-like grooves and ridges that grind up the food into even smaller pieces, much as molars do for mammals.

Birds that eat hard foods such as insects and seeds have very strong gizzards lined with particularly hard grinding plates, whereas birds that feed on soft foods such as fish, meat, fruit and nectar do not need as strong a gizzard. A number of birds such as the Common Ostrich, ducks and geese swallow small pieces of grit and stone that collect in the gizzard and help in the grinding process.

The time taken for food to pass through the digestive tract varies from less than half an hour, in the case of berries ingested by thrushes, to half a day or more for less easily digested food. Indigestible pieces of plastic, mistaken for food, have been known to remain in the gizzard for months. In species that feed on bones, exceptionally strong enzymes and acidic gastric juices in the proventriculus dissolve bones rapidly before the food reaches the gizzard. A shrike can digest a mouse in just three hours, while the Bearded Vulture is able to digest an entire cow vertebra in two days.

UNUSUAL DINING COMPANY

In some cases, birds and animals work together to form seemingly unlikely symbiotic feeding partnerships. These partnerships can be **parasitic**, where one species benefits to the detriment of another (rare in birds); **commensal**, which literally means 'eating at the same table' and refers to situations where one species benefits while the other is neither benefited nor adversely affected; or **mutual**, where both animals benefit.

Egrets and cattle

Cattle Egrets are aptly named as they are often found following cattle in open fields, benefiting from feeding on the insects disturbed by the cows. This habit gave rise to their generic name *Bubulcus*, which is Latin for 'ploughsman' or 'herdsman'. This association evolved in Africa and egrets can often be seen following large herbivores such as buffalo or elephant. Fork-tailed Drongos also forage close to large herbivores to feed on disturbed insects.

Cattle Egrets often follow elephants and other herbivores to take advantage of the insects disturbed as they walk.

Large herbivores such as giraffe and zebra benefit from the oxpeckers' parasite removal service, while the oxpeckers get an easy meal.

Oxpeckers and large herbivores

Oxpeckers are often found perched on the backs of large mammals such as giraffe, zebra and rhino, using their exceptionally sharp claws to cling onto the host and their short, stiff tails as props. While the parasites hiding in the animals' fur provide the birds with a nutritious meal, the host also benefits from the feathered 'parasite removal service'.

The two species of oxpecker have different bills for removing parasites in different ways. While the Red-billed Oxpecker has a slender, flattened bill used for 'scissoring' parasites and grease from the host's hide, the Yellow-billed Oxpecker has a stouter bill used to pluck them off. Both species also use their beaks to trim open wounds and scars from which they sip blood – often to the detriment of the host. The hosts provide a platform for courtship displays and even provide hair for lining oxpeckers' nests.

The stout bill of the Yellow-billed Oxpecker (BELOW) plucks parasites from animals' fur; the Red-billed Oxpecker (ABOVE) uses a scissoring action with its slender, flattened bill.

Honeyguides and honey badgers

The Greater Honeyguide's Latin name is, appropriately, *Indicator indicator*, which acknowledges its habit of leading the way to beehives, either for the benefit of humans or honey badgers. The bird utters a distinctive chattering note when leading, and hops about anxiously within the observer's view. If followed, it will fly ahead through the trees straight towards the beehive. Here, the bird waits patiently until the hive has been broken open, then greedily feasts on the exposed honeycomb and bee larvae.

Honeyguides have developed special strategies to cope with their idiosyncratic eating habits: not only does their tough skin give them some immunity to bee stings, they also carry highly specialized bacteria in their gut that makes them the only birds in the world able to digest beeswax. Many myths have sprung up around honeyguides: one being that, if selfish followers do not leave the bird any honey, it will lead them to a black mamba next time in revenge!

A Southern Pale Chanting Goshawk shadows a honey badger, waiting to grab any prey it disturbs.

Southern Pale Chanting Goshawks and honey badgers

A number of different bird species are known to forage in association with the honey badger, one of the regulars being the Southern Pale Chanting Goshawk. The goshawk closely shadows the badger as it actively forages, often swooping down quickly to grab disturbed prey such as insects, rodents and reptiles before the badger managers to reach them.

Waders and crocodiles

Another distinctive association between birds and other animals occurs between various waders and crocodiles. The Blacksmith Lapwing, Common Sandpiper and Water Thick-knee all feed near crocodiles lying on riverbanks, and are known to pluck parasites from their backs as they bask in the sun. Reputedly, some of these birds have been seen entering crocodiles' mouths to pick remnants of food from between their teeth or leeches from the lining of their mouths. It is thought that crocodiles don't regard them as a tasty snack because they benefit from having decaying food and parasites removed.

Hornbills and mongooses

Yellow-billed and Red-billed hornbills are known to follow dwarf mongooses as they forage for food, snatching up small prey items that try to escape from them. In the event of danger, hornbills give alarm calls that also serve to warn the mongooses – another good example of co-operative teamwork between different species. There are even records of hornbills waiting at the entrance of mongoose burrows in anticipation of going foraging for the day.

UNUSUAL DIETS

Some birds have a highly specialized and unusual choice of menu, and may employ ingenious methods in catering for these exotic tastes.

Egyptian Vultures – scrambled eggs: Egyptian Vultures are unusual in their ability to make use of tools to access their prized food: nutritious ostrich eggs. They achieve this by throwing or dropping stones onto the eggs in order to break open the thick shell.

Bearded Vultures – bones and marrow: Bearded Vultures are among the few birds capable of eating bones, their diet consisting of up to 70 per cent bone and marrow. Like circus sword-swallowers, they are able to swallow whole bones of up to 25 cm long, and sharp ends don't seem to give them discomfort. Larger bones are first dropped with great accuracy from a height of about 60 m onto exposed rocky surfaces to break them into smaller pieces and allow the bird access to the nutritious marrow. Bones often have to be dropped repeatedly before they eventually break. The nutritional value of the Bearded Vulture's specialized diet is about 15 per cent higher than that of the predominantly meat diet of most carnivorous birds.

Cuckoos – hairy caterpillars: Cuckoos are unusual in that they specialize in eating hairy caterpillars. Although caterpillar hairs often have irritant properties and are known to form a thick lining in their stomachs, the birds appear to suffer no ill effects from such an extraordinary diet.

Honeyguides – beeswax: Honeyguides are the only species of bird in the world that are able to digest beeswax, exploiting special bacteria in their gut in order to achieve this.

Egyptian Vultures are unique in using stones as tools to crack open the hard shells of Common Ostrich eggs.

Diderick Cuckoos have an unusual preference for hairy caterpillars, and are somehow immune to the irritant effect of their prickly prey.

Palm-Nut Vultures – palm nuts: The Palm-Nut Vulture has the peculiar reputation of being the only raptor in southern Africa that feeds mostly on fruit. The flesh of raffia palm fruits provides this bird with a rich, oily and nutritious meal, which it scrapes off using its sharp-edged, broad bill – well adapted for this specialized function. Although predominantly vegetarian, Palm-Nut Vultures also feed on a variety of other foods, including fish, crabs and lizards.

Hooded Vultures – dining on droppings: Hooded Vultures are known to follow packs of wild dogs and pick through their droppings in search of tasty morsels.

Bat Hawks – bats on the wing: Bat Hawks, as their name implies, specialize in feeding on bats (as well as on swifts and swallows). They hunt at dusk in the open sky and are exceptionally agile flyers. They skillfully catch their prey in flight, using their talons, then transfer it to their mouths and swallow – all this while still on the wing.

Crowned Eagles – poached poodles: In rare cases, Crowned Eagles have been caught poaching small poodles from gardens in towns!

Marabou Storks – flamingo chicks: Marabou Storks are known to prey on flamingo chicks, which are an easy target as the parents are unable to defend them.

Grebes – feather filters: Grebes are known to swallow their own feathers, which accumulate between the gizzard and the intestine. The feathers act as a filter, preventing the passage of sharp fish bones and indigestible food remains, which they then regurgitate.

An insectivorous Woodland Kingfisher is about to swallow, rather surprisingly, a bat.

11 THE MYSTERIES OF MIGRATION

Barn Swallows on telephone wire

MIGRATION IS ONE OF THE ENDURING MYSTERIES OF ORNITHOLOGY.
Although the complexities of migration are still not completely understood, a lot more is known now than in the past. Two thousand years ago, Aristotle believed that swallows hibernated in the mud during winter. A hundred odd years ago, people thought that they flew to the moon at the end of summer. Cuckoos were believed to change into hawks in winter, which explained why they disappeared as it got colder. Gradually, as a result of bird ringing and laboratory studies, the movements of birds and the mechanisms governing their migrations have become better understood. Although there has been vast progress since Aristotle's time, and neither the mud nor the moon are now regarded as realistic non-breeding destinations, there still remain many unanswered questions relating to migration.

Derived from the Latin word *migrare* meaning 'to move from one place to another', migration can be defined as predictable journeys, usually from a breeding area to a non-breeding area and back again. Over 130 bird species in southern Africa are migrants, either undertaking epic intercontinental journeys, or moving within the African continent itself.

WHY MIGRATE?

By migrating between hemispheres, birds are essentially moving from one extravagant summer banquet to another. After making the most of the food supplies in one area in order to raise their brood, they flee the extreme weather and food shortages of an impending winter to spend the non-breeding season in another summer destination. The major drawback in undertaking these journeys is the enormous distance that separates their destinations, and the high risks involved in undertaking such an enterprise twice a year.

Given the risks associated with the journey, one might question whether the promise of abundant food supplies and good weather justifies embarking on such a hazardous venture at all. For many species, the costs greatly outweigh the benefits and migration is not an option. For others, making the journey – albeit hazardous – significantly improves their chances of survival and, most importantly, allows them to raise more offspring than if they stayed in one place. These are the birds that 'pack their bags and go'.

A classic example of such a migrant is the Curlew Sandpiper, which breeds in the high arctic tundra. It takes full advantage of the long daylight hours and abundant food sources during the short summer months there, and then flies to the warmer southern hemisphere during the non-breeding season. A number of other well-known migrants and the issues surrounding their epic journeys are discussed in this chapter.

TO GO OR NOT TO GO?

Whether a species of bird is migratory or not is largely influenced by what it eats. Migration is usually characteristic of insect-eating birds, as the abundance of insect life varies greatly between seasons. Insects are most active and more plentiful during the warm summer months.

The most common migrants are aerial foragers such as swallows, swifts, bee-eaters and nightjars, which feed in the open sky. Their invertebrate prey is highly susceptible to seasonal weather conditions in this exposed environment, and is far more common during the more favourable summer months. These birds generally migrate in the autumn when prey supplies start to diminish. Many waders are also migratory, as the invertebrates on which they feed are more numerous during the warm summer months.

The insectivorous Southern Carmine Bee-eater is a typical intra-African migrant.

However, not all insectivorous birds are migrants. In contrast to aerial feeders, the more terrestrial insect-eaters that forage in wooded areas or close to the ground in leaf litter, such as thrushes, robin-chats and babblers, do not need to migrate: in this leafy, sheltered environment, which is more protected from extreme weather conditions than the open sky, insects are more readily available year round.

The fish-eating African Malachite Kingfisher (LEFT) is resident, while the insectivorous Pygmy Kingfisher (RIGHT), is an intra-African migrant.

Generally, fruit-eating birds such as barbets and turacos are resident in one place throughout the year, as their food supply is available in one form or another all year and they need move only short distances to access new food sources. Seed-eating birds such as finch-larks and sandgrouse are nomadic rather than migratory. Their movments are discussed in greater detail on page 162. Another example of the influence of diet on migration is found among certain kingfishers: the fish-eating Malachite Kingfisher is resident, as its food supply is fairly constant all year round, while for the insectivorous African Pygmy Kingfishers, it is clearly best to migrate.

DIFFERENT DESTINATIONS

While some bird species are 'high-flying' international travellers, migrating vast distances between continents every year, others are more local travellers and remain within the African continent itself. Depending on their travel destinations, our southern African migrants can be classified into three main categories.

The Curlew Sandpiper, a Palaearctic-African migrant, flies thousands of kilometres from Northern Siberia to southern Africa and back again each year.

Travelling abroad: Palaearctic-African migrants

Palaearctic-African migrants are true avian globetrotters, migrating between continents each year. These species have the longest and most arduous of journeys, flying thousands of kilometres from Europe and Asia all the way to Africa and back again. They are primarily non-breeding migrants, arriving in southern Africa at the onset of summer after having bred further north. They escape hostile conditions that engulf their breeding grounds in winter to spend the non-breeding season making the most of the abundant and varied menu that southern African habitats have to offer. Palaearctic species that migrate to southern Africa include numerous waders, the Steppe Eagle, Steppe Buzzard, White Stork, European Roller, Barn Swallow and several terns.

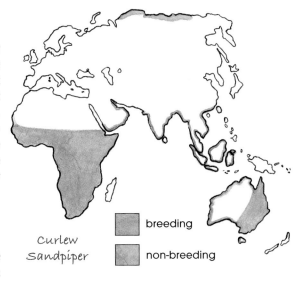

Curlew Sandpiper

breeding

non-breeding

African wanderers: intra-African migrants

Intra-African migrants do not venture abroad like the Palaearctic-African migrants, but rather move annually between their breeding and non-breeding grounds within the African continent. Most migrants take advantage of the abundance of food during the wet season, migrating between the northern and southern parts of the continent and the equatorial regions.

Of the migrants that visit southern Africa, many breed here, such as the Wahlberg's Eagle, African Reed-Warbler, Greater Striped Swallow and many of the cuckoos. In contrast, others such as the Abdim's Stork breed north of the equator, then migrate south during the non-breeding season. Some species, including the Red-chested and Diderick cuckoos, breed in both northern and southern Africa, then converge to spend the non-breeding season in the tropics.

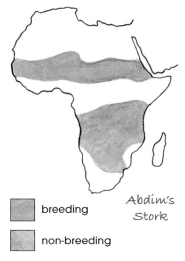

Abdim's Stork

breeding

non-breeding

The Abdim's Stork breeds north of the equator and then migrates south.

Domestic travellers: local migrants

Local migrants are birds that do not undertake long, epic journeys, but rather travel locally over shorter distances within one area. For example, the Mangrove Kingfisher breeds inland from the coast during the summer months, then migrates back to its coastal mangrove habitats at the end of the breeding season. 'Altitudinal migration' occurs in birds that make the most of the good conditions for breeding at high altitudes in mountainous areas during the warm summer months, then descend to lower altitudes in winter when conditions become too hostile. Examples of such birds include the African Stonechat, White-starred Robin and Sentinel Rock-Thrush.

NON-MIGRATORY MOVEMENTS

In contrast to true migrants, which follow a fairly set route from their breeding to their non-breeding areas and back again each year, several other species follow more random, unpredictable movements that are not strictly classed as migration.

The Red-billed Quelea is nomadic and is known to track available food supplies.

A wandering life

Many species are better suited to a wandering lifestyle. 'Irruptions' occur when birds move *en masse* into new areas, usually in response to drought, short food supplies or overcrowding in one area. The Red-billed Quelea is a notorious example of this, where hundreds of thousands of birds move from one area to another in enormous, plague-like flocks.

In arid zones, species such as sandgrouse and larks are known to survive the extremely dry conditions by adopting a more nomadic lifestyle. They do this by following food supplies closely, and will often unpredictably move into areas that provide such food resources, usually in response to rainfall.

Refugees on the run: pursuing, escape and spreading movements

Pursuing movements are found in birds that follow or track food resources. For example, raptors, storks, rollers and bee-eaters may follow locust swarms or other insects disturbed by fire. Sunbirds track the opening of flowering plants, while queleas flock to areas with sufficient seeds.

Life-threatening conditions such as drought, floods or the depletion of available food may force certain birds into what are known as **escape movements**, when small or large

The invasive Common Mynah has spread widely since it was introduced to South Africa a century ago.

numbers of birds may leave an area to escape from extreme conditions. For example, swifts may travel long distances in order to avoid the onslaught of a thunderstorm.

Some bird species gradually expand their former distribution by moving into new areas over time, and these are referred to as **spreading movements**. For example, the Hadeda Ibis and the exotic Common Mynah have, over the past several decades, spread to many areas beyond their former distribution, the Mynah threatening to out-compete indigenous species.

LONG-DISTANCE TRAVELLERS

The planning of any long journey requires decisions about the best route possible, taking into account the distance, time available, places to stop en route and the particular mode of transport. Migratory species have plotted their flight plans so that each species follows the most efficient route possible.

Flyways and stop-over sites

Just as we follow concrete highways that link destinations, so too do migratory birds follow apparently distinct aerial flyways that cross and link entire continents, and that only become apparent to us when they are being traversed by flocks of migrating birds. These fly-way routes are the most efficient paths for birds to follow, taking into account the distance, geographical barriers and landmarks, favour-able winds, stop-over sites, and their particular flying style – be it soaring or flapping.

At various points along their migration route, birds make use of specific stop-over sites where they rest and 'refuel' before the next strenuous stage of their journey, much as we make use of petrol and fast-food stops on long-distance road journeys. Many species have a series of historical stop-over sites that have been used repeatedly over the years. These are known to be a reliable source of food, and the locations of these stop-over sites are thought to be passed on from generation to generation. However, with increasing habitat destruction, these vital sites are at risk, and there is a real danger that destruction of such sites may have a serious impact on the many migratory birds that have come to rely on them.

Steppe Buzzards follow distinct fly-ways in their epic migrations.

Funnel-shaped migration

Thin land corridors linking different continents may be characterized by a funnel-shaped concentration of thousands of migratory birds, all avoiding a sea crossing. Classic examples of this phenomenon occur over Israel and Gibraltar, which act as giant avian 'funnels', as millions of birds migrate between their nesting grounds across Eurasia and their non-breeding sites in Africa twice a year. Interestingly, these land corridors are used mainly by larger birds such as raptors and storks as they rely heavily on thermals of warm air rising over the land to fuel their flight; they consequently often have to follow longer routes so as to avoid sea crossings, as thermals do not form over the ocean.

Thirty-five species of diurnal birds of prey fly over Israel during these autumn and spring migrations, including hundreds of thousands of European Honey and Steppe buzzards, while Lesser Spotted, Steppe and Booted eagles, Pallid and Eurasian marsh-harriers also use this popular route. It is also a favoured flight path used by thousands of White Storks and White Pelicans.

Some larger migratory birds follow funnel-shaped migratory paths that converge over specific land bridges.

Looping and leapfrogging

Rather than migrating to and from their breeding grounds along the same route, certain birds follow a circular migratory route known as 'loop migration'. For example, the Red-backed Shrike migrates in a giant loop from Europe to central and southern Africa and back again in an anti-clockwise direction. Arctic Terns are

INSIDE INFO

VAGRANTS

When battling under extreme weather conditions, migratory birds may sometimes be blown off course or lose their sense of direction and arrive at completely unintended destinations. Ironically, their misfortune often makes them celebrities in the birding world, and they are quickly surrounded by the birding *paparazzi*, their every movement being monitored, photographed and reported in the birding press!

Examples of vagrant birds turning up in South Africa include the Little Blue Heron, Greater Sheathbill, Eleonora's Falcon, American Purple Swamphen, Hudsonian Godwit, Buff-breasted Sandpiper and White-throated Bee-eater. Vagrant birds often tend to be juveniles; young, inexperienced birds are known to be at greater risk of getting lost on migration than older, more experienced individuals, which are better able to correct for deviations from their flight paths.

known to complete an epic loop migration route of up to 50 000 km from their Arctic breeding grounds all the way to the Antarctic and back again every year. It is thought that birds make use of favourable tail winds on these circular routes, allowing them to expend less energy when flying extremely long distances.

'Leapfrog migration' is an apt term to describe an intriguing phenomenon whereby certain bird populations that breed furthest north fly furthest south in the non-breeding season, leapfrogging over other populations of the same species which breed at intermediate latitudes. Although there are a number of different theories to explain this phenomenon, it is still very much of a mystery. The reasons that have been put forward to explain leapfrogging include competition for food, escaping predation, as well as making the most of climatic differences that influence the birds' breeding success. An example of a species that 'leapfrogs' is the Common Ringed Plover, where birds from the Arctic are thought to fly to southern Africa, by-passing other populations on the equator.

THE RECORD HOLDERS

Many migratory birds have flown their way to fame by achieving remarkable records on their annual journeys:

* **The longest journey**: Arctic Terns are true endurance flyers, known to migrate up to an astounding 50 000 km from their breeding grounds in the northern Arctic tundra to the Antarctic pack ice and back again each year. Given that Arctic Terns may live for perhaps 25 years, it is possible that they may fly up to one million kilometres in their lifetimes. They also hold the record for experiencing more daylight hours than any other animal.

* **The fastest non-stop journey**: Bar-tailed Godwits migrating from the Alaskan tundra to New Zealand hold the record for non-stop migration. After breeding in the tundra, they embark on a non-stop flight of 11 600 km, travelling south across the Pacific Ocean and arriving on New Zealand's North Island only some six days later, having flown at an average speed of 80 kilometres an hour!

* **Highest flyers**: Most small migratory birds fly less than 2 000 m above sea level, most waders at between 2 500 and 3 000 m above sea level, while larger birds such as raptors are known to migrate at an altitude of 4 000–6 800 m. The record holder for the highest flight is the Rüppell's Vulture; one was hit by an aeroplane over the Ivory Coast at an altitude of 11 300 m. (By comparison, Mt Kilimanjaro, the highest mountain in Africa, reaches a height of 5 895 m at its summit.)

Arctic Terns

ENDURING THE JOURNEY

Given the gruelling physical challenges faced by all migratory birds, they need to be as prepared as possible for the challenges that lie ahead on their journey. As with any serious athlete, prior training and preparation are required.

Fuel for the flight

Many migratory birds have remarkable endurance, regularly making extremely long, non-stop flights without landing to feed or rest. These birds draw on large fat reserves to fuel their long and physically punishing journeys. To do this, they indulge in eating binges known as 'hyperphagia', consuming enormous quantities of food before leaving, and building up extra fat stores in their bodies. Fat is an exceptionally efficient fuel because it contains up to five times more energy than protein, and has the added advantage of being much lighter. Some passerines can increase their body weight by up to 50 per cent before leaving, while some of the waders, such as the Sanderling and Ruddy Turnstone, spend at least a month fattening up to increase their stores by as much as 90 per cent. During the physically arduous flight, the stored fat deposits are gradually used up and birds eventually have to break their flight and spend time 'refuelling' at stop-over sites en route.

By contrast, many large species such as raptors and storks, which migrate only short distances between stop-over sites, do not need to fatten up before leaving as they are able to stop and feed en route. These birds' daily flights are necessarily short, as they are determined by thermals produced by hot, rising air that develop only during the heat of the day.

A flock of Curlew Sandpipers fattens up in preparation for the long journey.

The Steppe Eagle doesn't need to store fat for the journey as it stops frequently to feed along the way.

Built for travel

To cope with the extreme demands of long-distance flight, migratory birds have had to evolve a number of specialized adaptations.

The wings of migrants are generally longer and narrower than those of resident species, as a more streamlined shape is better for long-distance flight. This is evident when comparing the narrower, pointed wing shape of the migratory bee-eaters with the more rounded wings of the resident species. Similarly, the Marsh-Warbler, which migrates long distances from Europe to southern Africa each year, has narrower wings than its relative, the African Reed-Warbler, which migrates shorter distances within the African continent.

Migrant birds are also remarkably well adapted to coping with low levels of oxygen when flying at high altitudes where the air is thin. In addition to having normal 'low altitude' haemoglobin (the red blood cells that carry oxygen), high-flying migrants have also evolved special 'high-altitude' haemo-globin which ensures that they have an adequate oxygen supply. While most mammals are able to adjust gradually to changes in altitude over a period of time, migrating birds don't have the time to acclimatize and their special-ized haemoglobin allows them to cope well with sud-den changes in altitude.

An extreme weight-saving technique in some migrant waders is the partial reabsorption of some of their digestive organs, such as their liver and intestines, which are not needed on long flights. These are then 'revived' again when the birds stop to refuel.

It has been suggested that bristles at the base of the beak act as a built-in speedometer, as birds are sensitive to the speed of the wind mov-ing over them as they fly. This allows birds to gauge their flight speed and remain at the optimal pace for migrating long distances – neither top speed, as they would exhaust them-selves too quickly, nor so slowly that the journey takes too long.

The wings of the migratory Southern Carmine Bee-eater (TOP) are longer and narrower than the more rounded wings of the resident White-fronted Bee-eater (ABOVE); an adaptation for flying long distances.

A flock of Curlew Sandpipers

Different modes of travel

Because migrants vary greatly in size as well as in wing and body shape, they make use of different types of flight, using the most efficient-means of saving energy.

❚ Large birds such as wildfowl, pelicans and storks often **fly in V-formation, bow-shaped formation** or in **simple oblique lines**. Flying in another bird's slipstream has been shown to save up to 20 per cent in energy – a significant saving when flying long distances.

❚ Another energy-saving means of flying for large birds such as storks and raptors is to **soar using thermals**, since flapping flight would cost them more than three times as much energy (*see* Chapter 1, page 22). Such thermals may take birds up to 6 300 m (vultures can soar up to almost 12 000 m), and allow them to fly with little effort for dis-tances of some 7 000 km at speeds reaching nearly 80 km/hour. One limitation of relying

Sanderlings migrate at night when the air is cooler and calmer, allowing for more efficient flight.

on thermals is that flying time is restricted to that time of day when thermals occur, and birds are often grounded for periods in between. They also cannot fly efficiently at night. In addition, they have to avoid crossing large expanses of water, where thermals do not form, preferring to make detours in order to use land corridors.

Most of the smaller birds migrate using **flapping flight**, as they are not able to soar as larger birds do. Although flapping flight uses huge reserves of energy, birds are able to fly faster and for longer periods of time than birds that soar, allowing them to reach their destinations more quickly. Many birds save energy by using **bounding flight**, where they close their wings and 'freewheel' between bouts of flapping (*see* Chapter 1, page 19).

While large birds that rely on thermals for flight have to migrate during the day, many species that are usually diurnal choose to migrate at night. These include waders, most insect-eating passerines such as bee-eaters and warblers, as well as ducks, geese and cuckoos. For many birds, **flying at night is an energy-saver** as the air is cooler, denser and calmer, which allows for more efficient flight; and birds are also less likely to fly into headwinds or to be blown off course. Flying in the cool of night also reduces water loss, which can be a significant limiting factor on long flights. Flying at night is an obvious advantage for birds that use the stars for navigation, while for species undertaking long flights, travelling both day and night results in significant time gains.

A SENSE OF DIRECTION

It has taken explorers and scientists thousands of years to develop and perfect our modern instruments of navigation, from a rudimentary compass to high-tech geographical positioning systems. Birds have had to evolve their own highly complex internal navigation systems – a sophisticated and intuitive combination of both physical cues, such as landmarks and the position of the sun and stars, and intangible cues, such as those derived from an innate internal compass and an ability to detect the Earth's magnetic fields.

Although much progress has been made in understanding birds' astounding ability to navigate, there is still much to be learned about this phenomenon.

Inherited or learned?

An intriguing question is how birds migrating for the first time know where to go – is this a learned or inherited ability? Many observations and experiments have shown that both the inclination to migrate, as well as the route to follow on migration, is largely inherited rather than learned. This is supported by the fact that young birds leaving on migration either before or after their parents, still manage to find their way on their first epic journey without parental guidance. The case of migratory cuckoos, whose chicks are raised in a foster family of non-migratory birds of an entirely different species, demonstrates that migratory instincts in this family must be inherited.

Migration is instinctual in species such as cuckoos, which are raised by non-migratory foster parents.

Another example of the inherited nature of migration was discovered by conducting experiments on captive birds. Such captive migrants displayed what is known as 'migratory restlessness' at the time that they would normally be departing. The agitated birds hopped and fluttered on their perches, facing the exact direction in which they would be flying on migration. This restlessness often lasted for the duration of the migratory period, decreasing when the wild birds would be reaching their resting areas. This migratory restlessness is particularly obvious in diurnal birds that migrate at night, as they show restlessness during a time when they would otherwise be sleeping. Long-distance migrants have been shown to display more restlessness compared to short-distance migrants. Interestingly, when long-distance migrants were hybridized with short-distance migrants, a transitional restlessness resulted. Further experiments showed that such birds also inherited a knowledge of migration routes.

However, 'learning from experience' should not be underestimated, and experienced birds are known to be better able to adjust and correct for changes en route (for example, if blown off course) than young, inexperienced birds. It is thought that young birds gradually integrate all the cues that they experience on their first journey to form a 'mental map' of the trip, allowing them to navigate, rather than simply orientate, on subsequent trips.

The magnetic compass

The Earth acts like an enormous magnet, producing a magnetic field that varies in angle over its entire surface, producing more magnetic force at the poles than at the equator. Unlike humans, who are unable to detect the Earth's magnetic fields, birds are highly sensitive to these fields and are able to align themselves accordingly on migration. It has recently been proposed that it is the occurrence of trace metal elements in the brains of birds that allows them to respond to magnetic fields.

ORIENTATION VERSUS NAVIGATION

In order to find their way, birds make use of two similar, yet distinct methods: compass orientation and goal orientation (also known as 'true navigation'). Compass orientation is basic direction finding, and allows birds to determine a broad compass direction. For example, a bird will know whether to fly north, south, east or west, but will not necessarily be able to find a particular place in that direction. Compass orientation is usually an innate ability.

Goal orientation, on the other hand, involves true navigation skills and allows birds to find and follow a particular route. This is a more advanced ability. Birds are able to determine their direction at each stage of the journey by making use of a range of different cues, and are thus able to find their way to specific areas or places. Aspects of navigational skill are generally learned and improved upon through experience, with older birds being more skillful navigators.

The sun compass

Many species are known to use the position of the sun in the sky to direct their flight paths. This was first discovered in the 1950s by the German biologist Gustav Kramer, who found that caged starlings with a good view of the sun showed migratory restlessness in the same direction that wild migratory starlings would be following. On overcast days, however, they were not able to orientate themselves.

In order to use the sun as a compass, birds have had to evolve the remarkable ability to compensate for its ever-changing position, both on its daily movements across the sky, as well as its varying position in the sky at different times of the year. The sun is used as a navigational cue by diurnal migrants, as well as many nocturnal migrants that take off at dusk, orientating themselves by the sunset.

Many birds are also able to detect ultra-violet light, which passes through clouds, and this may help them to track the position of the sun on cloudy days. The sun is not used as a compass only by migratory species on long-distance flights, but also by many resident species to orientate themselves in their everyday activities.

The star compass

Many species of migratory birds that travel at night are known to rely heavily on the stars to guide them on their journey. Experiments on captive migratory birds within a planetarium have shown that they make use of the star compass, orientating themselves accordingly as the artificial star pattern is moved.

Other cues

Birds are thought to make use of a number of other migratory aids, although some of these have yet to be proved conclusively. These include heightened powers of vision and sense of smell, recognition of landmarks, auditory cues such as waves breaking along the coast, and variations of barometric pressure. Most birds are able to draw on several different means of orientating themselves. For example, on cloudy nights when the stars are not visible, birds are able to orientate themselves according to the Earth's magnetic fields.

THREATS TO HABITAT

Flying long distances can be risky for birds. Even if they survive the many natural obstacles in their way such as harsh weather conditions, exhaustion or shortages of food, there are also human-related threats to contend with. Breeding or non-breeding grounds may have been affected by habitat loss or degradation, or much-needed wetland stop-over sites may have been drained, converted to fields, or covered in industrial waste. As if that weren't enough, birds must dodge bullets and avoid traps over the Mediterranean area and certain parts of Africa if they are to avoid the fate of several hundred million of their migratory comrades that are shot, caught and traded each year.

The only way to conserve migrants is to protect their existing breeding and non-breeding grounds and stop-over sites, and expand the existing global network of protected areas. A big step towards this was the establishment of the Bonn Convention, which addresses the transboundary conservation of migratory species. In addition, the RAMSAR Convention was formed with the aim of protecting wetlands of international importance. In theory, these conventions play an important role in protecting migratory waterbirds, but enforcing them is complicated by the trans-border political and economic co-operation required between member states in order for them to be effective.

Birds and planes: sharing airspace

During the migratory period, Israel faces a unique challenge: as well as having half a billion birds from three continents funnelling *en masse* across its skies, it also has the highest concentration of fighter aircraft in the world. Airspace becomes crowded, and sharing the skies is potentially fatal for both parties. Ironically, significantly more aircraft are lost to bird collisions than to enemy fire. More than 2 600 aircraft of all descriptions have been lost in this way since 1972. To prevent further disasters, the Israeli government has had to design strategies to prevent the flight-paths of birds and planes from overlapping. Among many tactics, 'Bird Plagued Zones' have been identified – these are particular areas favoured by migrating birds, and planes are prohibited from flying in these zones during the migration period.

Although South Africa doesn't face the same scale of threat from bird strikes, aircraft are still at risk near airports and a number of preventive measures have been put in place. The Endangered Wildlife Trust encourages falconers to fly their birds on airport grounds to scare birds away, while specially trained dogs play a similar role at ground level.

A dog patrols a runway as part of the Endangered Wildlife Trust's Airport Wildlife Hazard Management Project.

PALEARCTIC MIGRANTS

Raptors	Waders	Other Waterbirds	Passerines	Other species
Common Honey Buzzard	European Oystercatcher	Sabine's Gull	Barn Swallow	Common Cuckoo
Steppe Eagle	Common Ringed Plover	Corncrake	Common House Martin	European Nightjar
Lesser Spotted Eagle	Lesser Sand Plover	Spotted Crake	Sand Martin	European Swift
Booted Eagle *	Greater Sand Plover	Arctic Skua	Garden Warbler	Alpine Swift *
Steppe Buzzard	Caspian Plover	Long-tailed Skua	Common Whitethroat	Blue-cheeked Bee-eater
Montague's Harrier	Grey Plover	Pomarine Skua	Icterine Warbler	European Bee-eater *
Pallid Harrier	Crab Plover	Subantarctic Skua	Olive Tree Warbler	European Roller
Osprey	Red Phalarope	Lesser Crested Tern	River Warbler	
Hobby Falcon	Red-necked Phalarope	Sandwich Tern	Great Reed Warbler	
Sooty Falcon	Broad-billed Sandpiper	Common Tern	Marsh-Warbler	
Red-footed Falcon	Ruddy Turnstone	Caspian Tern	Sedge Warbler	
Amur Falcon	Common Redshank	Arctic Tern	Willow Warbler	
Lesser Kestrel	Marsh Sandpiper	Little Tern	Spotted Flycatcher	
Black Kite	Terek Sandpiper	Black Tern	Collared Flycatcher	
	Common Sandpiper	White-winged Tern	Red-backed Shrike	
	Green Sandpiper		Lesser Grey Shrike	
	Wood Sandpiper		Eurasian Golden Oriole	
	Little Stint		Yellow Wagtail	
	Great Snipe		Tree Pipit	
	Greenshank			
	Red Knot			
	Curlew Sandpiper			
	Sanderling			
	Black-winged Pratincole			
	Ruff			
	Eurasian Curlew			
	Bar-tailed Godwit			
	Whimbrel			

Common Sandpiper

Table excludes migrant seabirds.
* These species also have resident populations.

INTRA-AFRICAN MIGRANTS

Raptors	Waterbirds	Passerines	Other
Wahlberg's Eagle	Striped Crake	White-throated Swallow	African Cuckoo
Yellow-billed Kite	Open-billed Stork	Blue Swallow	Red-chested Cuckoo
	Dwarf Bittern	Pearl-breasted Swallow	Black Cuckoo
	African Crake	Red-breasted Swallow	Levaillant's Cuckoo
	Streaky-breasted Flufftail	Greater Striped Swallow	Great Spotted Cuckoo
	Lesser Gallinule	Lesser Striped Swallow	Jacobin Cuckoo
	Lesser Moorhen	South African Cliff Swallow	Emerald Cuckoo
	Abdim's Stork	Banded Martin	Klaas's Cuckoo
	Yellow-billed Stork *	Black Saw-wing Swallow	Diederik Cuckoo
	Black-winged Lapwing	African Golden Oriole	Black Coucal
	Senegal Lapwing	Capped Wheatear	Rufous-cheeked Nightjar
	Collared Pratincole	African Reed- Warbler	Pennant-winged Nightjar
	Damara Tern	Copper Sunbird	African Black Swift
		Chestnut Weaver	White-rumped Swift
		Red-headed Quelea	Horus Swift
		African Paradise Flycatcher	Little Swift
		Violet-backed Starling	Alpine Swift *
		Dusky Lark	Pygmy Kingfisher
			Woodland Kingfisher
			Grey-hooded Kingfisher
			Olive Bee-eater
			Southern Carmine Bee-eater
			Broad-billed Roller
			African Pitta

Red-chested Cuckoo

12 TRACKS AND SIGNS

Greater Flamingos

BIRDS LEAVE A RANGE OF OFTEN CRYPTIC SIGNS BEHIND THEM AS THEY GO ABOUT THEIR EVERYDAY LIVES. A scattered row of tracks left in the sand, a berry-stained dropping, a line of tiny beak holes 'stitched' into wet mud, a few dishevelled feathers lying in the grass – all these signs point to bird activity. By decoding these avian clues, we can learn much about the birds that left them.

SIGNS IN THE SAND: DECIPHERING BIRD TRACKS

Endless trails zigzagging back and forth in the sand may all seem the same at first glance: bird tracks. Although it is often difficult to identify the tracks of a specific bird species – unless you happen to see them being made – they can usually be identified to family or group level. For example, tracks near a wetland may be identified as those of a heron or egret, but it wouldn't be possible to confirm which species made them. Tracks can give us much useful information about a bird's behaviour, habits and diet.

HOW FEET INFLUENCE TRACKS

The shape of a track is determined by the shape of a bird's toes. Birds only walk on their toes, while the rest of the foot extends halfway up the leg. What looks to us like a bird's knee is actually its ankle.

WHAT TO LOOK OUT FOR

When you come across a bird track, ask the following questions:
- How big is the track?
- How many toes can you see?
- How many toes point forwards?
- Is there a back toe? If yes, is it long or short?
- Can you see signs of webbing?
- Is the track on the beach, along a river bank, in a wetland, on a mudflat, on a dune, in the bushveld, in your garden?

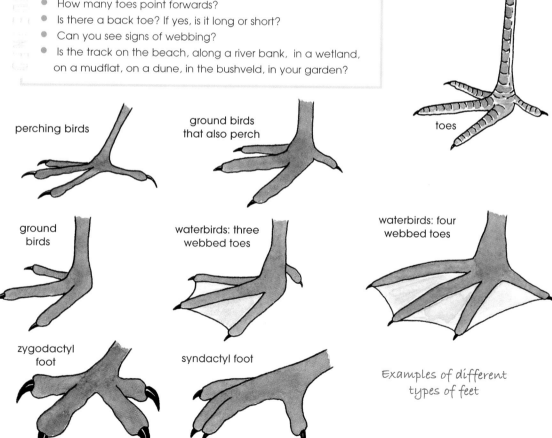

ankle

foot

toes

perching birds

ground birds that also perch

ground birds

waterbirds: three webbed toes

waterbirds: four webbed toes

zygodactyl foot

syndactyl foot

Examples of different types of feet

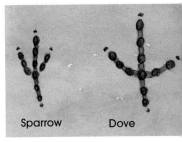

Perching birds: Birds that spend most of their time in trees and bushes have feet that are adapted for **perching**: three toes pointing forward, and a long back toe. These long toes are specially adapted for gripping firmly onto branches as they move through the trees. Perching birds that also spend time foraging on the ground, such as doves, have toes that are more widely splayed, as this is better for walking.

Examples of birds with this track type include robin-chats, thrushes, shrikes, weavers, doves, sparrows and waxbills.

Sparrow Dove

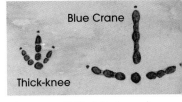

Ground birds: The feet of true ground birds are adapted for **walking and running**: three toes pointing forward, either no back toe or a very small back toe. Because they spend all their time on the ground, they don't need a long back toe for gripping a perch, and are in fact unable to perch. The back toe of ground birds has either been lost completely over the years, or is so small that it doesn't touch the ground when the bird walks and so doesn't leave an imprint. A long back toe would hinder the bird when it runs.

Examples of birds with this track type include waders, bustards and korhaans, and cranes.

Blue Crane

Thick-knee

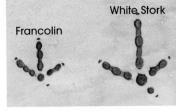

Ground birds that also perch in trees: These birds have three toes pointing forward and a shortish back toe (often at an angle). They spend most of their time on the ground, and need to perch only when they roost. They have strong, spread toes that are adapted for **walking and running**. They do not need a long back toe for gripping onto branches as arboreal birds do. Their short back toe is used only for grasping a perch when roosting. On firm ground, the back toe may not leave an imprint.

Examples of birds with these tracks are francolins and spurfowl, guineafowl, Secretary-birds and White and Marabou storks.

Francolin White Stork

Waterbirds with three webbed toes: The webbing acts as a paddle, pushing against the water when the bird swims, helping to propel it forward.

If the sand is too firm or compact, the webbing is sometimes not visible in a track. In some species, the small back toe may leave a slight impression.

Examples of birds with this track type include ducks, geese, flamingos, gulls, Pied Avocets, penguins and terns.

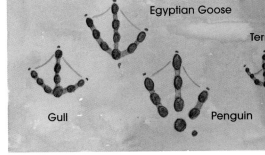

Egyptian Goose Tern Gull Penguin

FEET VARIANTS

Zygodactyl feet: Some birds have what are known as 'zygodactyl' feet: two toes face forwards and two face backwards. For birds that are agile climbers and often cling to vertical branches, such as woodpeckers, barbets and parrots, having two toes at the back instead of one provides extra support. Owls and the Osprey are able to rotate their outer front toe backwards, which increases the spread of the toes when hunting, making them more effective hunters. Many of these birds spend little time on the ground, so their tracks are not often seen.

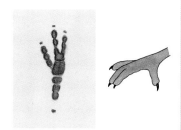

Syndactyl feet: In the feet of some birds, the second and third toes are fused for part of their length. This 'syndactyl' arrangement is common among kingfishers and hornbills.

  Waterbirds with four webbed toes: It is thought that the extra webbing helps these birds propel themselves more effectively as they dive to catch their prey underwater (birds with three webbed toes remain mainly on the surface).

Examples of birds with this track type include pelicans, cormorants, African Darters and gannets.

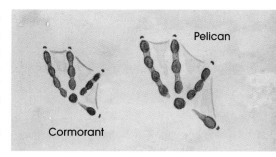
Pelican
Cormorant

Unusual tracks: One of the more unusual tracks belongs to the Common Ostrich, which has only two toes on each foot: the first and second toes have been lost over time as the ostrich has evolved the optimum foot for running, making it the fastest runner of all birds. Its large third toe and strong claw are used for running, while the small fourth toe helps the bird to balance when walking slowly.

The coot has lobed webbing along each individual toe.

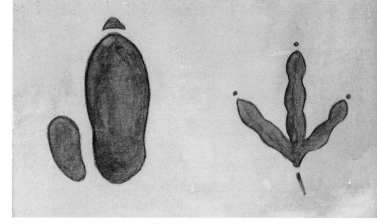

A Common Ostrich track (LEFT) *and a coot track* (RIGHT)

Tracks on different surfaces: Tracks can look very different depending on the surface on which they are imprinted. The shape and size of the track, as well as the amount of detail visible, can vary greatly. The best surfaces for clear, detailed tracks are damp sand, firm muddy earth or a thin layer of loose 'dust' on a firm substrate. However, tracks are often found on ground that is not ideal: it is either too hard, where the imprints are faint and lacking in detail; or too soft and sandy, where tracks are loose and without detail. For this reason, it is best to follow the trail for a while until you find the clearest print.

Below are some examples showing how tracks can vary, depending on the surface of the ground:

Firm, moist ground – clear track, good detail; individual toe pads can be seen.

Loose, dry sand – track loses detail; track looks larger as loose sand collapses inwards.

Hard ground – only a faint imprint can be seen; detail not clearly visible.

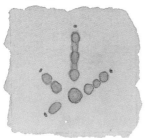

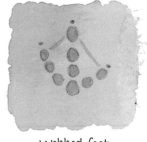

Hard ground covered by thin layer of dust – clear track; detail such as individual toe pads and wrinkles under the foot clearly visible.

unwebbed foot

webbed foot

TRAILS

Walking and running: The difference between walking and running can be seen in the spacing between individual tracks. When the bird runs, its stride gets bigger and the linear tracks are spaced further apart (below left). When it walks, the tracks are closer together (below right).

Hopping: When birds hop, they leave paired tracks opposite each other. Birds that might leave such tracks include larks, sparrows and buntings.

Toe drag marks: When some birds walk or run, the middle front toe may scrape the ground, leaving toe drag marks in the sand.

DROPPINGS AND PELLETS

Taking a close look at bird droppings and pellets may not appeal to people quite as much as admiring the bird itself, but they are well worth examining, as they can provide an informative glimpse into the lives of the birds that left them. They contain evidence of what the bird has been eating, reflecting seasonal variations in diet, while piles of droppings or pellets can be a clear sign of where birds roost, nest or choose to dine.

Droppings

Bird droppings vary greatly in shape and size, have different contents and consistencies depending on the species that produced them, and vary from season to season. Droppings are either scattered at random throughout a bird's range, or accumulate in piles at feeding, roosting or nesting sites.

ANATOMY OF A BIRD DROPPING

Unlike mammals that excrete urine and faeces through two separate openings, birds excrete both together through a **single opening, the cloaca**. For this reason, a typical bird dropping will usually have a distinctly dark section, consisting of faeces, and a whitish section, consisting of urine (or uric acid). In order to conserve liquid, a bird's body re-absorbs most of the water contained in the urine before it is excreted, and the uric acid is therefore fairly solid.

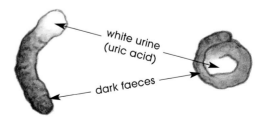

white urine (uric acid)

dark faeces

Examples of bird droppings

A DIVERSITY OF DROPPINGS

Although droppings are usually not distinct enough to be linked to a specific species, you can usually tell which 'group' of birds they belong to by examining their contents and looking at their shape. For example, the droppings of seed-eaters look very different from those of insect-eaters, which in turn look different from those of carnivorous birds such as raptors.

The **droppings of insect-eating birds** are hard, usually dry, and contain the small, indigestible remains of insect parts. If you look closely, you can often see the small, shiny, hard carapaces or limbs that could not be digested.
Examples of insect-eating birds are wagtails, swallows, martins, thrushes and robin-chats.

The **droppings of seed-eating birds** are generally semi-solid and well formed. They often contain seeds that the bird was not able to digest, which have passed through the gut undamaged. Some plant species rely on their seeds being exposed to strong stomach acids in the bird's gut, which stimulate germination. Birds also play an important role in seed dispersal, as they usually excrete seeds at a distance from the tree from which they were eaten.
Examples of seed-eaters are sparrows, doves and finches.

Spur-winged Goose

The **droppings of birds living on vegetation**, grazing mainly on plants and grass, are usually sausage-shaped. They contain compact plant remains, and coarse fibres can usually be seen if you look closely or break the droppings apart.
Examples of such birds are ducks, geese, francolins and guineafowl.

The **droppings of carnivores and scavengers** are either completely liquid or semi-liquid white splashes. Most of the hard parts of their food is regurgitated as pellets, so that droppings contain mainly urine and liquid faeces. In the case of raptors, the white liquid faeces is squirted out as a jet. It is almost impossible to identify different species from these splashes alone, and other signs such as pellets or lost feathers would need to be examined.
Such birds include raptors, herons, cormorants, storks and African Darters.

FUNCTIONAL FAECES

In many birds, particularly passerines, the droppings produced by young chicks are excreted in a **faecal sac**, which encloses the dropping in a layer of mucus. This enables the parents to remove the faeces without their breaking apart, and to drop the sac away from the nest – thereby helping keep the nest area clean and hygienic, as well as making it less visible to predators.

In some species, such as mousebirds and turacos, the parents eat the droppings of their young chicks, as they still contain nutrients that the chick is unable to absorb. **Droppings in the nest**, or piled up below the site, clearly show that not all birds make an effort to keep the nest area clean. Both dove chicks and adults deposit their droppings right in the nest. These droppings are thought to serve an important function: they act as cement to bind the flimsy twig nest together, a structural improvement that becomes increasingly important as the chicks get bigger.

A Cape Sugarbird keeps the nest area clean by removing its chick's droppings, which are enclosed in a gelatinous sac.

Whitewashed rock indicates the presence of a Southern Bald Ibis colony.

Namaqua Dove chicks huddle in their fouled nest. The droppings help to cement the flimsy structure.

Marabou Storks defecate on their legs to keep cool, hence their whitewashed apperance.

In many hole-nesting birds such as the Green Wood-Hoopoe and kingfishers, nest sanitation is also not a priority. Layers of droppings and food remains accumulate in their nests, which soon become unhygienic and foul-smelling.

An **accumulation of droppings** in one place is a sure sign of either a roosting or nesting site. White raptor 'splashes' are also usually highly visible below nesting or feeding sites.

Vultures and Marabou Storks sometimes have a layer of 'whitewashing' covering their legs. When the weather is hot, they use their **droppings to keep cool**: they defecate down their legs in a process known as 'urohydrosis'.

BIRD, REPTILE OR MAMMAL?

At first glance, similar-sized droppings of birds, reptiles and mammals may look very similar. Bird and reptile droppings are particularly difficult to distinguish as both groups excrete their urine and faeces together, producing droppings with dark and light sections. However, there are certain tell-tale characteristics.

In **bird droppings** (below), the white urine section usually merges with the dark faeces section, or covers it.

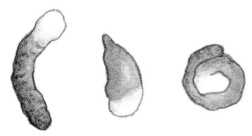

In **reptile droppings** (below), the white urine does not merge with the faeces, but forms a distinct white or cream cap at one end of the dropping. The urine cap can usually be separated easily from the faeces.

Mammal droppings (below) usually have at least one tapering end. Urine and faeces are excreted separately in mammals, so there is no white urine section attached to the dropping at all.

Pellets

Many birds regurgitate the hard, indigestible remains of their food in pellets. These pellets can contain a wide range of objects from feathers, bones, fur, seed husks, insect and other invertebrate pieces, to lizard and fish remains. Pieces of plastic even make their way into the pellets of some birds – a rather disturbing sign of the times. All these indigestible food parts collect in the bird's gizzard, where they are compacted together to form a hard pellet before being regurgitated.

/ Fur and feathers and other **softer materials** often **enclose harder objects** such as bones and insect parts, making the pellet easier to regurgitate. Pellets are also covered in a layer of lubricating mucus that helps them to slide easily up the gullet, and which is visible if the pellets are found fresh.

Owl pellets usually contain small bones and insect parts embedded in a mass of rodent fur.

/ One could reasonably question **why birds produce pellets** at all, and why the hard, indigestible parts of their food are not just excreted with their droppings. Reasons for this are that the pyloric opening (the junction between the stomach and intestine) is just too narrow for large objects to pass through. Because birds do not have teeth, they are not able to chew their food into small pieces. They either swallow the

HOW TO EXAMINE PELLETS

- Soak the pellet in water for about half an hour to soften it.
- Tease it apart gently using tweezers.
- Separate the contents (bones, insect pieces, fur, etc.).
- Use a hand lens (or microscope) to help identify the contents.

A single Barn Owl pellet contains the bones of its recent rodent meal.

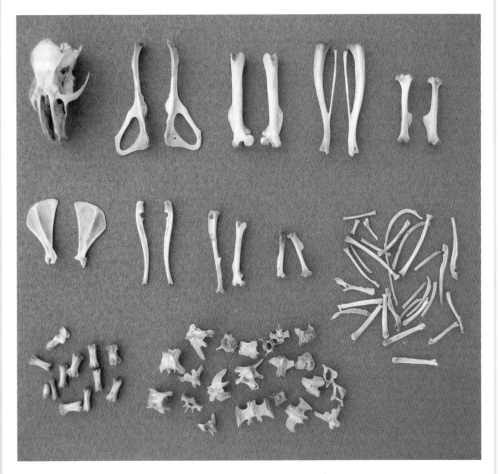

food whole, or tear it into pieces small enough to swallow. In addition, the stomach acid of some birds is not strong enough to break down or digest hard substances such as bone and the chitin in insect parts. Because these large, indigestible pieces cannot fit through the pyloric opening, they have to be regurgitated.

Which birds produce pellets? Although it is well known that birds of prey produce pellets, a wide variety of other bird species do so too, including herons, gulls, crows, waders, shrikes, storks, skuas, kingfishers and bee-eaters. However, because the pellets of these species are often small and crumble fairly easily, they are seldom found.

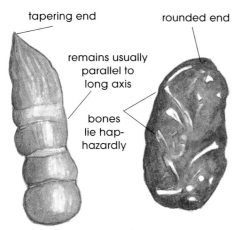

tapering end   rounded end

remains usually parallel to long axis

bones lie hap-hazardly

A mammal dropping (LEFT) and a bird pellet (RIGHT).

⫽ The **pellets of owls** are the most interesting to examine. This is because owls swallow their prey whole or in large sections, so bones are regurgitated in one piece and can sometimes be used to identify the species eaten. The pellets of other raptors may contain bone fragments (as opposed to whole bones) as the flesh is usually torn off the bones first, or eaten with small bone pieces.

⫽ How does one **distinguish bird pellets from animal dropping?** Bird pellets containing fur, feathers and pieces of bone can sometimes be confused with carnivore droppings, which may contain similar materials. However, there are differences: in mammal droppings, the remains usually lie parallel to the long axis of the dropping, which is often twisted with at least one tapering end. The remains in bird pellets lie haphazardly in the pellet, which is not twisted and usually has more rounded ends.

OTHER SIGNS OF BIRD LIFE

In addition to leaving a trail of tracks, droppings and pellets behind them, birds also leave a number of other interesting signs as they go about their everyday activities.

Bill marks in the sand

Waders probing for food leave distinctive bill marks in the sand along beaches and in estuaries. Triangular marks in sand along the beach are usually made by a gull beak. Other signs of scavenging activities, as well as gull tracks, may also be found in the area. Lines of tiny holes in the mud may be feeding trails left by some of the smaller waders, which 'stitch' the ground while walking.

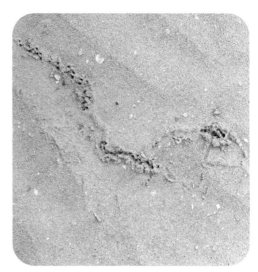

Waders often leave rows of 'stitching' bill marks as they search for food beneath the ground.

Shrike larders

Shrikes store their food by impaling it on thorns and barbed wire, or jamming it into the angles of branches. Because they don't have long talons to hold their prey while dismembering it, impaling the prey helps to hold it securely.

Feather signs

▌ A **pile of feathers**, even if there is no body, usually shows either the site of a kill, or where a predator stopped to pluck a bird.

▌ **Raptors** pluck feathers from their prey using their sharp beaks to reach the flesh. This leaves a hole or broken section at the base of the quill which can usually be seen if the feather is examined closely.

▌ When plucking their bird prey, **small carnivorous mammals** such as mongooses and genets either bite through the base of the feathers, or pull the feathers out in mouthfuls. This usually leaves the quills broken and the feathers damaged.

▌ If you find a **single**, **undamaged feather** it could either have been moulted by the bird or lost during preening.

A pile of Burchell's Coucal feathers found at a kill site

Bases bitten through by small mammal

Base of quill damaged when plucked by raptor

The bitten-off bases of these Natal Francolin feathers indicate it was plucked by a small mammal.

Indentations in the bark left by woodpeckers searching for insects.

Woodpecker holes

Woodpeckers leave tell-tale indentations in the wood when searching for insect prey below the bark of trees.

Sand/dust baths

A shallow scrape in loose, dusty ground may indicate the site of a bird's dust bath. Look out for tracks or loose feathers around the site that can help you identify the species of bird.

Tracks leading to a nest

A number of trails leading in the same direction and converging at a particular point could indicate the nest site of a ground bird. Such trails are most obvious in fairly open areas such as beaches, where coastal birds often nest above the highwater mark, and in coastal dunes.

Grass and leaf stripping

Many members of the weaver family tear strips off leaves, grasses and reeds to use for building their nests. This leaves the plants looking shredded and untidy.

Natal Francolins dust-bathe either in soft sand (ABOVE) or in more stony ground (BELOW).

13 WHAT'S IN A NAME?

LATIN NAMES AND THEIR SEMANTICS MAKE A FASCINATING STUDY AND, ALTHOUGH SEEMINGLY OBSCURE, they can often be even more descriptive than the common names of birds. For example, the scientific name of the Ruff, *Philomacus pugnax,* means 'fond of fighting', in reference to the males' territorial behaviour, while the Common Fiscal is called the 'butcher bird' after its genus *Lanius,* which means 'butcher'. This chapter lists 25 well-known southern African birds and explains the derivation of their scientific names.

We also take a brief look at explorers of the past and others who have had birds named after them. For example, did you know that Klaas's Cuckoo was named by Le Vaillant after his Khoi Khoi servant, who presumably found the bird in 1784? Have you ever wondered who the Burchell was whose name the Coucal adopts, or who Stanley (as in Stanley's Bustard) was? Did you know that Captain George Shelley, after whom Shelley's Francolin was named, in turn named the Woodward Barbet after Robert Woodward, who was an Anglican missionary, or that the Swedish collector Johan Wahlberg, after whom the Wahlberg's Eagle was named, was trampled to death by an elephant?

SOME SOUTH AFRICAN BIRDS AND THEIR LATIN NAMES

African Finfoot
Podica senegalensis
Pous (Gr), genitive *podos*: a foot; hence *podicus* (L): belonging to the foot; a reference to the long, lobed toes, the lobes acting as paddles instead of webbed feet, which gives it greater agility when walking on land. *-ensis* (L): suffix meaning 'belonging to'.

African Hobby
Falco cuvierii
Falx (L), genitive *falcis*: a sickle. A reference to the birds' curved talons. *Cuvierii* derived from the French zoologist and author MF Cuvier (1775–1838), brother of the better known Baron Georges Cuvier. The name 'hobby' is said to come from Old French *hober*: to move.

Bearded Vulture or **Lammergeier**
Gypaetus barbatus
Gups (Gr) genitive *gupos*: a vulture; *aetos* (Gr): an eagle; *barbatus* (L): bearded; a reference to the black feathers under the beak that form the 'beard'. The name 'lammergeier' comes from the German *lamer*, lambs, and *geier*, a vulture; they are reputed to carry off live lambs for food, but this has never been verified.

Brown-throated Martin
Riparia paludicola
Ripa (L): the bank of a stream or river; *riparius* (L): one that frequents the banks of streams; *palus* (L), genitive *paludis*: a marsh, swamp; *colo* (L): inhabit; martins make nests by tunnelling into the banks of streams or other sandbanks.

Bearded Vulture

Burchell's Starling
Lamprotornis australis
Lamprotes (Gr): brilliance; *ornis* (Gr): a bird; a reference to the bird's metallic green plumage with a purple sheen. *Australis* (L): southern. Named after Dr WJ Burchell (1782–1863), a naturalist and author who explored South Africa in 1811; he is better known from having Burchell's Zebra named after him, but other birds such as a coucal, courser and sandgrouse also carry his name.

Caspian Tern
Sterna caspia
Sterna (L): a tern; *caspia*: derived from the Caspian Sea, where it is common and widespread.

Burchell's Starling

Cattle Egret
Bubulcus ibis
Bubulcus (L): a ploughman who ploughs with oxen; in a more general sense, a herdsman. It is an allusion to this egret's habit of following buffalo or herds of domestic cattle, searching for the insects that are disturbed by their hooves, or perching on their backs to find the insects that plague the cattle.

Cattle Egret

Common Chaffinch
Fringilla coelebs
Fringilla (L): a small bird; *coelebs* from *caelebs* (L): unmarried, refers to either a bachelor or a widower; sometimes chaffinches gather in single-sex flocks, and at one time it was thought that the females migrated south, leaving the males behind.

Common Fiscal
Lanius collaris
Lanio (L), tear; *lanius* (L): a butcher; a reference to the shrike's habit of impaling its prey on a spike or thorn, hence the colloquial name 'butcher bird'.

European Nightjar
Caprimulagus europaeus
Caprimulgus (L): a milker of goats; can be used to mean a countryman. There was an ancient and ill-founded belief that nightjars could suck milk from domestic goats, hence an alternative name for the bird is 'goat-sucker'.

Golden-tailed Woodpecker
Campethera abingoni
Kampe (Gr): a caterpillar; *therao* (Gr): hunt, chase animals; this woodpecker feeds on various insects and grubs, including cater-pillars and ants. It is named after M Abingdon, (1784–1854), the fifth Earl of Abingdon, an English naturalist.

Goliath Heron
Ardea goliath
Ardea (L): a heron. In the Old Testament, Goliath was the Philistine giant who was killed by the the young Israelite boy, David, with a stone from his sling. This is a big heron, up to 1,5 m in height.

Goliath Heron

Jackass Penguin
Spheniscus demersus
Sphen (Gr): a wedge; *-iscus* (L): a diminutive suffix derived from the Greek *iskos*: a little wedge.

Jackass Penguin

Marabou Stork

This refers to the shape and shortness of the wings. *Demergo* (L): submerge; *demersus* (L): depressed. The English name is derived from the penguin's donkey-like call. Newly named the African Penguin.

Marabou Stork
Leptoptilos crumeniferus
Leptos (Gr): slender; *ptilon* (Gr): a wing; *crumena* (L): a small money purse or bag, usually hanging from the neck; *fero* (L): to bear; an allusion to the naked pink throat-pouch hanging from the neck, a rather ugly appendage for the purpose of thermo-regulation; *marabout* (Fr): a priest, can mean an ugly/grotesque, misshapen man.

Narina Trogon
Apaloderma narina
Hapalos (Gr): soft, tender; *derma* (Gr): the skin; taxidermists have found this bird to be a problem as the delicate skin breaks easily and the feathers are liable to fall out; all trogons are alike in this respect. This species is named after a Hottentot girl, Narina, who lived in the Knysna District of the Western Cape from about 1765 to 1782; little is known about her but she evidently died young.

Pennant-winged Nightjar
Macrodipteryx vexillarius
Macros (Gr): large, long; *dis* = *di* (Gr): two; *pterux* (Gr): a wing; refers to the two considerably elongated primaries of the male. During courtship flight these trail behind the main wing like pennants or flags. *Vexillarius* (L): a standard-bearer.

Pintailed Whydah
Vidua macroura
Vidua: derived from Whydah, a small town on the coast of Dahomey in western Africa, where these birds were first discovered. *Macros* (Gr): long; *oura* (Gr): the tail.

Ruff
Philomachus pugnax
Philos (Gr): loving; *makhe* (Gr): battle, combat; *pugnax* (L): fond of fighting, quarrelsome; there is a ritual of fighting among the male birds that forms part of the courtship/lekking ceremony.

Secretarybird

Secretarybird
Sagittarius serpentarius
Sagitta (L): an arrow;
sagittarius (L): an archer, a
bowman; named for the
way their upright carriage
and dignified stride
reminded people of an
archer about to fire an
arrow. *Serpent* (L): snake.
The bird is associated with
snakes, which form a large
part of its diet; the name
'secretary' is an allusion to
the spray of quills project-
ing from the back of the

head, reminiscent of the
old-fashioned quill pens
that were tucked behind
the ears of secretaries.

Southern Bald Ibis
Geronticus calvus
Geron (Gr): genitive *geron-
tos*, an old man; *icus* (L):
suffix meaning 'belonging
to' or 'pertaining to'; *calvus*
(L): bald.

Swainson's Spurfowl
Pternistes swainsonii
Pterna (Gr): the heel;
pternistes (Gr): one who
strikes with the heel; the
bird's legs have sharp spurs
that they use in fighting.
Named after W Swainson,
FRS (1789–1855), a much
travelled English zoologist
and artist.

Wandering Albatross
Diomedia exulans
Diomedes, according to
Greek legend, was ship-
wrecked on the coast of

Italy, where he remained
and died an old man; his
companions were turned
into birds. *Exul = exsul* (L):
an exile, a wanderer.

**Black-crowned
Night-Heron**
Nycticorax nycticorax
Nux (Gr), genitive *nuktos*:
night; *korax* (Gr): a raven.
Usually seen only at night,
this heron has a harsh,
crow-like call. Species
name reinforces genus:
night = dark = black.

Wilson's Storm-Petrel
Oceanites oceanicus
Oceanus (L): the ocean.
Derived from Okeanos, in
Greek mythology the god of
the river, which was
believed to encircle the
Earth; *-ites/icus* (L): suffix
meaning 'having to do
with', 'belonging to'. The
Storm-Petrel is the smallest
of the ocean birds and
spends most of its life at sea;
sailors associate its appearance with stormy weather.

Yellow-billed Oxpecker
Buphagus africanus
Bous (Gr): an ox or bull;
phagein (Gr): to eat; a reference to their habit of clinging to the backs of large
animals like buffalo, rhino
and antelope, where they
climb about searching for
ticks, flies and other insects
on which they feed.
Africanus (L): of Africa.

Southern Bald Ibis

Burchell

William John Burchell (1781–1863) was an English explorer/naturalist who went to the Cape of Good Hope in 1810, and undertook a major exploration of the interior of South Africa between 1811 and 1815, during which he travelled more than 7 000 km through largely unexplored country. He published his two-volume work, *Travels in the Interior of Southern Africa*, in 1822 and 1824. Burchell was the first European to describe the White Rhinoceros and has the Burchell's Zebra named after him. He was renowned as a meticulous collector, botanist and artist. Among the bird species named in his honour are the Burchell's Coucal, Burchell's Courser, Burchell's Sandgrouse and Burchell's Starling.

Delegorgue

Louis Adolphe Joseph Delegorgue (1814–1850) was a French hunter and naturalist who explored southern Africa between 1830 and 1839 for the British Natural History Museum. The Delegorgue's (now Eastern Bronze-naped) Pigeon was named after him. He also collaborated with Wahlberg.

Delegorgue

Heuglin

Theodor von Heuglin (1824–1876) was born in Ditzingen, Germany, where the local school is named after him. He became a mining engineer and ornithologist and spent some time in north-east Africa collecting natural history specimens. Heuglin's Robin (now named White-browed Robin-chat) was named after him.

Kittlitz

Friedrich Heinrich Freiherr von Kittlitz (1799–1874) was a Polish-born German artist, naval officer, explorer and ornithologist. His friend Eduard Rüppell (who in turn had the Rüppell's Korhaan named after him) encouraged his interest in natural history and they travelled together

to North America in 1831 to collect various specimens. Between 1826 and 1829 Von Kittlitz undertook a round-the-world journey collecting birds as well as vegetation off the coasts and islands of the Pacific. The Kittlitz's Plover is named aften him.

Kittlitz's Plover

Klaas

Le Vaillant named Klaas's Cuckoo after his Khoi Khoi servant, who presumably found the bird in 1784. Nothing further is known about him.

Le Vaillant

Francois Le Vaillant (1753–1824) was a French traveller, explorer, collector and naturalist. He was born in Dutch Guiana, the son of the French consul there. He was interested in birds from an early age and spent much of his time collecting specimens. He travelled to the Cape Province of South Africa in 1781, in the employ of the

Le Vaillant

Dutch East India Company. There he both explored and collected specimens, eventually publishing a six-volume book, *Histoire Naturelle des Oiseaux d'Afrique*, which is a classic of African ornithology. This work was published between the years 1801 and 1806 in Paris, and contained 144 colour-printed engravings. Over 2 000 skins were sent to Jacob Temminck (who in turn had the Temminck's Stint named after him), who financed his expedition. A large collection of his specimens is said to have been lost on one occasion when a Dutch ship was attacked and sunk by the English. The Levaillant's Cisticola as well as the Crested Barbet (*Trachyphonus vaillantii*) are named after him.

Roberts

J Austin Roberts (1883–1948) was a South African zoologist. He was born in Pretoria in 1883 and died in a traffic accident in 1948. During the first half of the twentieth century he was the most prominent ornithologist in southern Africa. He worked at the Transvaal Museum for 38 years studying birds. Although he did not have formal academic training, he received several high academic awards and an honorary doctorate. Roberts is best remembered for his *Birds of South Africa*, a landmark publication in African ornithology, which first appeared in 1940, and which was a best-seller in its numerous subsequent editions. The Roberts' Prinia (now Warbler) is named after him.

Shelley

Captain George Ernest Shelley (1840–1910), a nephew of the famous poet, was a geologist before he became interested in ornithology. He was edu-

Stanley's Bustard

cated in England and at the Lycee de Versailles, after which he joined the Grenadier Guards in 1863, retiring a few years later with the rank of captain. He wrote books on the birds of Egypt, and a review of sunbirds, a monograph of the Nectariniidae, in 1880. He collected in Africa, Australia and Burma, but suffered a paralysing stroke in 1906, which prevented him from travelling further. The Shelley's Francolin, with its distinctive call, is named after him.

Stanley

Edward Smith Stanley (1775–1851), the 13th Earl of Derby, was a zoologist and collector. He founded the Derby Museum, which was based partly on his specimen collection, including 318 bird species. He was President of the Linnaean Society and of the Zoological Society of London for over 20 years. The Stanley's (now Denham's) Bustard was named in his honour.

Stark

Arthur Cowell Stark (1846–1899) was a British physician and naturalist who travelled widely to collect birds. He was co-author with WL Scaler of the *Fauna of South Africa*.

He was killed by shellfire during the South African War at the siege of Ladysmith. The Stark's Lark is named after him.

Verreaux

Jean Baptiste Edouard Verreaux (1810–1868) was a French naturalist, collector and dealer. He worked for some time in South Africa's Cape Colony. Verreaux and his family traded in Paris from a huge emporium for stuffed birds and feathers, which they called the Maison Verreaux. They were ambitious taxidermists and became notorious for stuffing the body of an African chief. This controversial exhibit was on show in Barcelona until the end of the twentieth century, when the man's descendents demanded that it be returned for a decent burial. The Verreauxs' Eagle is named after him and his brother, Jules.

Wahlberg

Johan August Wahlberg (1810–1856) was a Swedish naturalist and collector. He studied chemistry and pharmacology at Uppsala in 1829 and worked in a chemist's shop in Stockholm. He travelled and collected widely in southern Africa between 1838 and 1856, sending thousands of specimens home to Sweden. He was eventually killed by an elephant on one of his travels. The Wahlberg's Eagle is named after him.

Wahlberg's Eagle

Wahlberg

Woodford

Colonel EJA Woodford (1761–1835) served in the British army in Europe between 1794 and 1817. He fought at the Battle of Salamanca in 1812 and at Waterloo in 1815, and commanded a battalion of the Coldstream Guards as part of the garrison at Cambrai around 1816. Woodford was also a natural history collector and dealt in bird art in London. The African Wood Owl (*Strix woodfordii*) is named after him.

Woodward

The Reverend Robert Woodward (1848–1897) and his brother John (1849–1899) were Anglican missionaries in Natal between 1881 and 1899. They were both deeply interested in ornithology and sent many specimens that they collected to the British Museum. They were co-authors of *Natal Birds*. The Woodward's (now Green) Barbet is named after them.

GLOSSARY

Albinism: lack of pigment in feathers due to a genetic inability to produce melanin. Albinistic birds are pure white.

Allopreening: the practice by one bird of preening another (*see* **Preening**).

Altricial: describes a chick that hatches with its eyes closed, with little or no down, that is incapable of walking and totally dependent on its parents for food.

Alula: a small group of feathers on the wrist joint of the wing used to prevent stalling during slow flight, e.g. when manoeuvring or landing.

Anting: the practice in some bird species of allowing ants to swarm across and between their feathers; formic acid produced by ants is thought to remove preen oil or repel insects.

Binocular vision: the area where the individual field of vision of each eye overlaps to form a single image.

Brood parasitism: the practice by one species of laying eggs in the nest of another species, which subsequently incubates the egg(s) and raises the foreign chick(s).

Brood patch: a patch of bare skin on the belly of an incubating bird which is placed against the eggs and helps to keep them at body temperature.

Cainism (siblicide): occurs where an older, larger chick kills its younger, smaller sibling.

Carotenoids: natural red, yellow, orange and pink pigments in feathers; a product of birds' diet.

Cloaca: the single opening through a bird's vent, used for excretion, laying eggs and copulation.

Clutch: the total number of eggs laid by a bird in one nesting.

Crop: a digestive organ used for the storage of food before it passes into the stomach.

Diurnal: active during the day.

Double-brooded: describes species that attempt to raise a second brood after successfully raising one brood in the same season.

Drumming: the sound produced by birds using their bills to hammer out a pattern on a hard surface, such as a dead tree trunk.

Eclipse plumage: the drab plumage into which the males of certain species moult after the breeding season.

Egg 'tooth': the hard, calcareous notch on the tip of the upper mandible of a chick's beak used for cracking the egg from the inside during the hatching process.

Faecal sac: small, gelatinous sac containing faeces excreted by nestlings, which is removed from the nest by the parents.

Fledgling: young bird that has left the nest but is not yet independent of its parents.

Flyways: specific routes or aerial 'highways' followed by migratory birds; usually the most efficient path to follow.

Frugivorous: fruit-eating.

Gape (flanges): the fleshy edges around the mouths of young chicks; usually brightly coloured in order to attract the parents' attention.

Gizzard: the muscular section of the stomach, often lined with hard ridges, in which food is ground up before passing into the intestine.

Granivorous: seed-eating.

Imprinting: the process whereby young chicks identify and bond with their parents shortly after hatching.

Iridescence: the metallic sheen on a bird's feathers caused by light reflected from the layered structure of the keratin.

Keratin: the tough and flexible protein of which feathers are made.

Leucism: unusual paleness of feathers.

Melanism: an excess of dark pigment (melanin) in feathers.

Migrant: a bird that migrates to and from breeding and non-breeding areas, usually on an annual basis.

Monocular vision: the visual field of one eye only.

Moult: the process of losing and renewing worn feathers.

Nictitating membrane: also known as the third eyelid, a membrane that sweeps sideways over the eyeball to keep the eye clean; gives added protection, and in diving birds allows them to see underwater.

Palaearctic: the geographical region including Europe, northern Asia and North Africa.

Passerine: a major order of small to medium sized birds. The passerines have also been called 'perching birds' or 'songbirds', although neither term is exclusive, the order being hard to define. Name derives from the Latin *passer*, a sparrow. All passerines share the following features: a foot with three toes in front, one behind, adapted for perching; hind toe at same level as front toes and never webbed. The chicks are always altricial.

Pecten: a special structure in a bird's eye that provides nutrients and oxygen to the retina.

Pellet: a regurgitated mass of undigestable matter such as fur, bones, feathers and insect parts.

Polyandry: an unusual mating system in birds in which a female pairs with several males. Found in the African Jacana and the Greater Painted-Snipe.

Polygyny: a mating system in which one male pairs with a number of different females. Found in the bishops and widowbirds, among others.

Precocial: refers to chicks that hatch well developed, with their eyes open, covered in a layer of down, and able to walk.

Preening: the process of drawing feathers through the bill in order to remove dirt and parasites to strengthen the barbs and to spread oil from the preen gland over the feathers.

Rhynchokinesis: refers to the ability of a bird's bill to bend along its length.

Salt glands: nasal glands in birds; in seabirds they excrete excess salt taken in with food or seawater.

Sexual dimorphism: differences in size, colour and plumage between the sexes in certain species.

Siblicide: (*see* **Cainism**)

Single-brooded: species that raise only one brood during each breeding season.

Synchronous hatching: clutches in which all the eggs hatch at the same time, as opposed to asynchronous hatching, in which the hatching of chicks is staggered.

Syrinx: a bird's voicebox.

Vagrant: a bird occurring outside its normal range.

Zygodactyl: a foot with two toes pointing forward and two toes pointing back.

BIBLIOGRAPHY

Attenborough, D. 1998. *The Life of Birds*. BBC Books, London.

Berthold, P. 1993. *Bird Migration*. Oxford Ornithology Series, Oxford.

Burton, R. 1990. *Bird Flight*. Facts on File, New York.

Burton, R. 1985. *Bird Behaviour*. Granada Publishing Limited, London.

Chantler, P and Driessens, G. 1995. *Swifts: A Guide to the Swifts and Treeswifts of the World*. Pica Press, Sussex.

Clancey, PA. 1985. *The Rare Birds of Southern Africa*. Winchester Press, Johannesburg.

Cleere, N and Nurney, D. 1998. *Nigthjars: A guide to Nightjars and Related Nightbirds*. Pica Press, East Sussex.

Collias, NE and Collias, EC. 1984. *Nest Building and Bird Behaviour*. Princeton University Press, New Jersey.

Dennis, N. 1999. *Birds of Southern Africa*. Sunbird Publishing, Cape Town.

Gill, FB. 1995. *Ornithology*. Second edition. W.H. Freeman & Company, New York.

Ginn, PJ, McIlleron, WG, and Milstein, P le S. 1989. *The Complete Book of Southern African Birds*. Struik Winchester, Cape Town.

Gotch, AF. 1981. *Birds – Their Latin Names Explained*. Blandford Press, Dorset.

Harris, T and Arnott, G. 1988. *Shrikes of Southern Africa*. Struik Winchester, Cape Town.

Harrison, JA, Allan, DG, Underhill, LG, Herremans, M, Tree, AJ, Parker, V and Brown, CJ. 1997. *The Atlas of Southern African Birds. Volume 1: Non Passerines*. BirdLife South Africa, Johannesburg.

Harrison, JA, Allan, DG, Underhill, LG, Herremans, M, Tree, AJ, Parker, V and Brown, CJ. 1997. *The Atlas of Southern African Birds. Volume 2: Passerines*. BirdLife South Africa, Johannesburg.

Hockey, P. 1996. *Birds in Action*. Struik Publishers, Cape Town.

Hockey, P and Douie, C. 1995. *Waders of Southern Africa*. Struik Winchester, Cape Town.

Johnsgard, PA. 1997. *The Avian Brood Parasites*. Oxford University Press, New York.

Kaplan, G and Rogers, LJ. 2001. *Birds – Their habits and skills*. Allen & Unwin, Crow's Nest, Australia.

Kemp, A and Kemp, M. 1998. *Sasol Birds of Prey of Africa and its Islands*. New Holland Publishers Ltd, Cape Town.

Kerlinger, P. 1995. *How birds migrate*. Stackpole Books, Mechanicsburg.

Lockwood, G. 2000. *Birding with Sappi and Geoff Lockwood*. Rapid Commerical Print Brokers and Publishers, Centurion.

Maclean, GL. 1990. *Ornithology for Africa*. University of Natal Press, Pietermaritzburg.

Maclean, GL. 1993. *Roberts' Birds of Southern Africa*. Sixth edition. The John Voelcker Bird Book Fund, Cape Town.

Newman, K. 1979. *Birdlife in Southern Africa*. Macmillan, Johannesburg.

Newman, K. 1983. *Birds of Southern Africa*. Macmillan, Johannesburg.

Perrins, CM and Middleton, ALA. 1985. *The Encyclopedia of Birds*. George Allen & Unwin, London.

Peterson, RT. 1968. *The Birds*. Time-Life International, Netherlands.

Pettingill, OS. 1970. *Ornithology in Laboratory and Field*. Fifth Edition. Academic Press Inc., Orlando.

Rowan, MK. 1983. *The Doves, Parrots, Louries and Cuckoos of southern Africa*. David Phillip, Cape Town.

Ryan, P. 2001. *Practical Birding*. Struik Publishers, Cape Town.

Short, LL. 1993. *The Lives of Birds*. Henry Holt and Company, New York.

Sinclair, I, Hockey, P and Tarboton, W. 1993. *Sasol Birds of Southern Africa*. Struik Publishers, Cape Town.

Sinclair, JC and Mendelsohn, J. 1981. *Everyone's Guide to South African Birds*. Struik Publishers, Cape Town.

Sinclair, I and Ryan, P. 2003. *Birds of Africa – south of the Sahara*. Struik Publishers, Cape Town.

Steyn, P and Arnott, G. 1990. *Hunters of the African Sky*. Struik Winchester, Cape Town.

Steyn, P. 1996. *Nesting Birds: The breeding habits of Southern African Birds*. Fernwood Press, Cape Town.

Stuart, C and Stuart, T. 1998. *A Field Guide to the Tracks and Signs of Southern and East African Wildlife*. Second Edition. Southern Book Publishers, Halfway House.

Stuart, C and Stuart, T. 1999. *Birds of Africa – from Seabirds to Seedeaters*. Southern Book Publishers, Rivonia.

Tarboton, W. 2001. *Nests and Eggs of Southern African Birds*. Struik Publishers, Cape Town.

Tarboton, W and Erasmus, R. 1998. *Owls and Owling in Southern Africa*. Struik Publishers, Cape Town.

Winterbottom, JM. 1971. *Priest's Eggs of Southern African Birds*. Winchester Press, Johannesburg.

INDEX